INTRODUCTION

The stunning success of Adolf Hitler's ground offensives during the first year of the Second World War relied on the use of fast but heavily armed and well-armoured tanks working together with motorised infantry and close air support. It was a formula initially replicated during the invasion of the Soviet Union in 1941 with still more staggering victories achieved in mere months.

When advancing German forces encountered the Soviet T-34 it suddenly became apparent that the technological arms race was much closer than anyone had realised and urgent action was needed. Development of heavier tanks with better weapons was speeded up to produce some of the war's deadliest and most iconic armoured fighting vehicles – the Tiger, the Panther and the Tiger II.

Although around 6000 Panthers were built, there were just 1347 Tigers and 492 Tiger IIs. The most produced German 'tank' was actually a turretless tank destroyer – the Sturmgeschü which more than 10,000 were ma were around 8500 Panzer IVs and Panzer IIIs. This compares to 50,C Sherman tanks and 84,000 Soviet

As the war ground on, Germany's panzer armies were forced on to the defensive, being driven backwards in the USSR during 1942, then in Italy beginning in September 1943 and from August 1944 in France too. Bombing raids on oil refineries and production facilities created crippling petrol shortages and the shattered remains of the once mighty German tank forces were eventually fighting within Germany itself and finally in small pockets of resistance. Even then, heavy tank destroyers such as the Jagdtiger and Jagdpanther, not to mention the 'big cats' themselves, proved formidable adversaries to the last.

Dan Sharp

ABOUT CLAES SUNDIN

Illustrator and author Claes was born in 1957 and lives in the southern part of Sweden. Since finishing four years of studies at the University of Uppsala, he has been active as a teacher, marketer, photographer and art director, among other occupations.

Since childhood, Claes has had a strong interest in everything concerning the combat vehicles of the Second World War and later. This interest stems from the time when he, as a boy of only seven, started building and collecting plastic scale models. Simultaneously, he has been an ardent draughtsman for as long as he can remember, as well as an accomplished CGI artist in more recent years. At present Claes is producing books, writing articles and lecturing. Up to now he has produced more than 2000 CGI profiles, mostly of aircraft, but also of Second World War armour.

His previously published books include: Luftwaffe Fighter Aircraft in Profile (1997), Deutsche Jagdflugzeuge (1998), More Luftwaffe Fighter Aircraft in Profile (2002), Luftwaffe Fighter Aircraft, Limited Edition (2011), Luftwaffe Fighter Aircraft, Profile Book No 1 (2013), Allied Fighter Aircraft, Profile Book No 2 (2013), Tiger and Panther Tanks (2014), Luftwaffe Fighter Aircraft, Profile Book No 3 (2014), Luftwaffe Attack Aircraft, Profile Book No 4 (2015), Profiles of German Tanks (2015), Luftwaffe Night Fighters, Profile Book No 5 (2016), Luftwaffe Fighter Aircraft, Profile Book No 6 (2016) and Luftwaffe Bombers, Profile Book No 7 (2017). In addition, he has provided aircraft and tank profiles, photo refinement, and artwork for many other books and papers.

Claes says: "As a long-time profile artist, I am well aware that a few of the profiles included in this publication will be the subject of some criticism. The reader, however, must acknowledge that all the profiles included are based on solid photographic documentation. I will always use at least one reference photo, more if available, of the subject. I seek the best photos available for the related close-up details as well.

"However, misinterpretations could naturally occur, especially regarding the colours I've chosen for the different profiles. One has to appreciate the difficulty of interpreting the colours from dated black and white photographs. But know that I have, together with my colleagues, made the utmost effort to determine the actual appearance and colouring of the individual vehicle profiles presented here."

CONTENTS

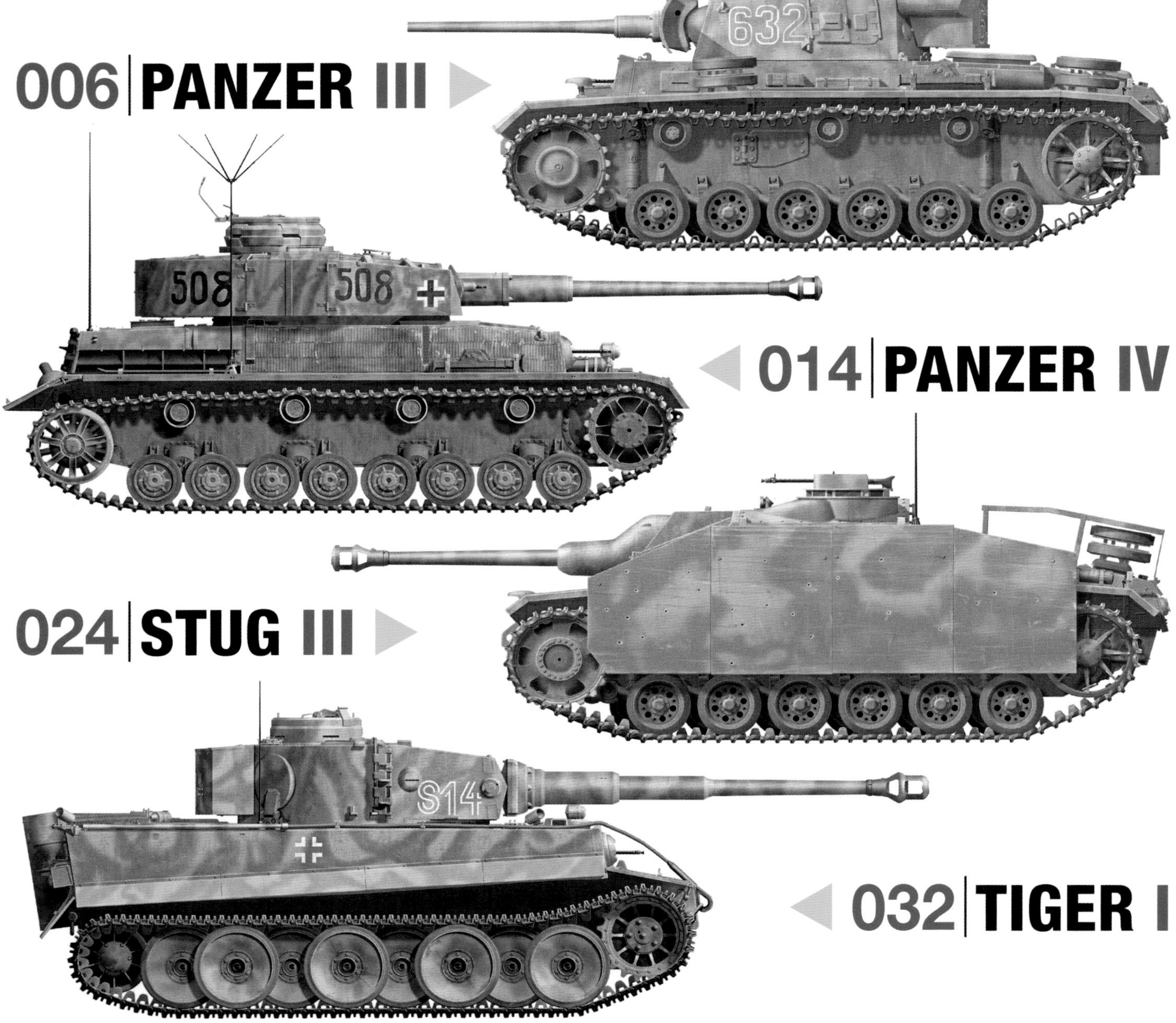

All illustrations:
CLAES SUNDIN

Editor:
DAN SHARP

Design:
SEAN PHILLIPS, ATG-MEDIA.COM

Production editor:
PAULINE HAWKINS

Publisher:
STEVE O'HARA

Published by:
MORTONS MEDIA GROUP LTD, MEDIA CENTRE MORTON WAY, HORNCASTLE LINCOLNSHIRE LN9 6JR
Tel. **01507 529529**

MORTONS

ISBN: 978-1-911703-39-6

T1
4 30
101
321
24 1
314

PANZERKAM

During the Blitzkrieg across France in 1940 and the invasion of Russia the following year, the Panzer III was at the forefront of the action as Germany's main battle tank. Within a few years, however, it had been left behind by rapid technological advances and was withdrawn from service before the war's end.

With the Panzer I having been conceived as a training tank and the Panzer II being a stopgap light tank, the Panzer III and Panzer IV were developed side by side as the German army's primary armoured fighting vehicles during the mid-1930s.

The Panzer III was intended to fulfil the role of main battle tank – using armour-piercing shells to defeat enemy tanks – while the Panzer IV was to be a support vehicle, using its short-barrelled cannon to fire high-explosive shells at enemy strongpoints and machine gun positions.

A specification for the Panzer III was issued by then-Oberst Heinz Guderian on January 11, 1934, which included a maximum weight of 16 metric tons and a 35km/h top speed. The width of the tank was restricted by the standard gauge of the German railways that would need to be used to transport it.

Four companies competed to design the vehicle – Daimler-Benz, Maschinenfabrik Augsburg-Nuremberg (MAN), Rheinmetall-Borsig and Krupp. Prototypes were constructed and Daimler-Benz was successful. The German army had wanted the Panzer III to be equipped with a 50mm anti-tank gun but this was not yet in production so the tank was instead equipped with the same 37mm gun then being supplied to the infantry – the 37mm KwK 36 L/45.

PFWAGEN III

When the first examples of the Daimler-Benz Panzer III Ausführung A appeared in 1936, the tank's turret ring had been designed in such a way that the 50mm gun could be fitted when it became available if so desired. Beside the main weapon, a pair of 7.92mm machine guns were mounted coaxially in a recessed mantlet and another 7.92mm machine gun was installed in a ball mounting on the hull's front plate.

The vehicle carried 120 rounds for the main gun and 4425 rounds for the machine guns.

The commander's cupola was a simple slotted ring and the turret had basic single-piece side hatches. Inside the hull, which had a maximum armour thickness of just 1.45cm in order to save weight, the commander was seated in the centre below the cupola. The gunner was in the turret to the left of the gun breach while the loader was on the right. At the front of the fighting compartment, the driver sat on the left and the radio operator/hull gunner on the right – with the tank's manually actuated five-speed (plus one-speed reverse) transmission positioned between them.

Driving the transmission and thereby the tracks via the front sprockets was a V12 Maybach 108TR engine, developing 250hp, positioned at the rear of the tank. ▶

PANZER III AUSF. L

Red 632 probably belonged to the 23rd Panzer Division, 1st Panzer Army. This is how it looked during Unternehmen Blau or 'Operation Blue' in the Caucasus, USSR, on June 30, 1942. Colour photos of this unit's Panzer IIIs suggest that the light-coloured patches were RAL 8020 Braun applied by the unit itself. The objective of Operation Blue was to seize the Caucasus oil felds. With their capture the Germans would deny the Soviets 82% of their crude oil production and at the same time address the problem of their own chronic fuel shortages. The 23rd Panzer Division advanced 11km during the first day and broke through the Soviet 21st Army's defences. However, the Russians had dug in and littered the area with minefields such that the division experienced heavy losses, with 10 tanks destroyed and 50 damaged. While the territorial gains were large, the Germans inflicted only minimal losses to the Soviets as the Red Army fell back into the vast expanses of the steppe and their next line of defence. Six months and 630,000 casualties later – of which 120,000 were German and Romanian – Operation Blue ended in failure and was abandoned.

PANZERKAMPFWAGEN III

The running gear itself, in addition to the sprockets, consisted of five medium-sized road wheels, a rear idler and a pair of return rollers on either side. The tracks were 36cm wide and suspension was by conventional coil spring. Weight was 15 tons and top speed was only 32km/h – 3km/h short of the speed required to meet the specification – and just 10 examples of the Ausf. A were built.

Fifteen examples each of the Ausf. B and C were built concurrently. The Ausf. B swapped the Ausf. A's coil springs for leaf springs to provide a small increase in speed. It featured eight small road wheels on either side attached to a pair of spring units arranged horizontally. An extra return roller was added too. This increased the vehicle's weight to very nearly the specification limit at 15.9 tons but speed did increase to 34.7km/h.

The Ausf. C was almost identical to the B except for utilising a different leaf spring arrangement – with one long horizontal spring unit and two shorter ones on either side.

Maximum armour thickness was increased for the Ausf. D – up to 30mm – and a new, lower, cupola with visors to protect the vision slits was fitted. A new gearbox with an extra forward gear was installed and eight-wheel suspension similar to that of the Ausf. C was used but with the smaller spring units slightly modified to sit at an inward angle. The extra armour took the vehicle's weight up to 19 tons. Twenty-five examples of the Panzer III Ausf. D were built during 1938.

The following year saw the introduction of the Ausf. E, with 30mm armour on the front and sides. The turret now featured side hatches with two-piece covers – these being easier to push open – and an external gun mantlet was fitted. One of the two coaxial machine guns was also deleted from the design. The hull was modified to incorporate escape hatches for the radio operator and driver too.

The earlier suspension systems had been replaced with a sturdier torsion bar arrangement and the number of road wheels was reduced to six. This would become the standard blueprint for all the Panzer IIIs that followed. The E also benefited from an improved powerplant, the 250hp 108TR being replaced by the 300hp HL 120TR, and the new Maybach Variorex pre-selector gearbox. This gave ▶

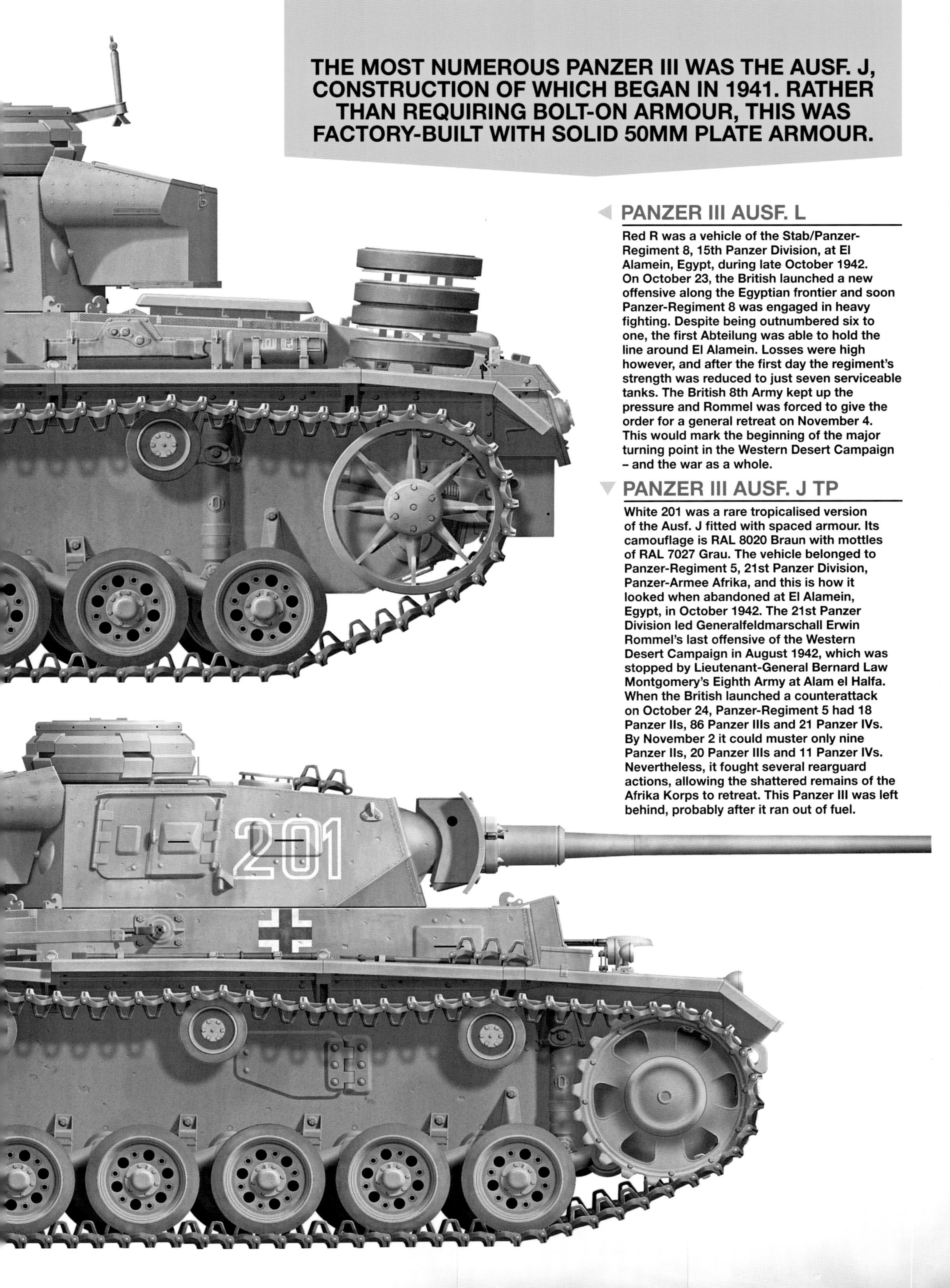

THE MOST NUMEROUS PANZER III WAS THE AUSF. J, CONSTRUCTION OF WHICH BEGAN IN 1941. RATHER THAN REQUIRING BOLT-ON ARMOUR, THIS WAS FACTORY-BUILT WITH SOLID 50MM PLATE ARMOUR.

PANZER III AUSF. L

Red R was a vehicle of the Stab/Panzer-Regiment 8, 15th Panzer Division, at El Alamein, Egypt, during late October 1942. On October 23, the British launched a new offensive along the Egyptian frontier and soon Panzer-Regiment 8 was engaged in heavy fighting. Despite being outnumbered six to one, the first Abteilung was able to hold the line around El Alamein. Losses were high however, and after the first day the regiment's strength was reduced to just seven serviceable tanks. The British 8th Army kept up the pressure and Rommel was forced to give the order for a general retreat on November 4. This would mark the beginning of the major turning point in the Western Desert Campaign – and the war as a whole.

PANZER III AUSF. J TP

White 201 was a rare tropicalised version of the Ausf. J fitted with spaced armour. Its camouflage is RAL 8020 Braun with mottles of RAL 7027 Grau. The vehicle belonged to Panzer-Regiment 5, 21st Panzer Division, Panzer-Armee Afrika, and this is how it looked when abandoned at El Alamein, Egypt, in October 1942. The 21st Panzer Division led Generalfeldmarschall Erwin Rommel's last offensive of the Western Desert Campaign in August 1942, which was stopped by Lieutenant-General Bernard Law Montgomery's Eighth Army at Alam el Halfa. When the British launched a counterattack on October 24, Panzer-Regiment 5 had 18 Panzer IIs, 86 Panzer IIIs and 21 Panzer IVs. By November 2 it could muster only nine Panzer IIs, 20 Panzer IIIs and 11 Panzer IVs. Nevertheless, it fought several rearguard actions, allowing the shattered remains of the Afrika Korps to retreat. This Panzer III was left behind, probably after it ran out of fuel.

PANZERKAMPFWAGEN III

PANZER III AUSF. L

Black 351 'Lore' of the 1st SS Panzer Regiment 'Leibstandarte SS Adolf Hitler', 4th Panzer Army, was involved in the fighting at Kursk during July 1943. The Leibstandarte were part of a southern pincer movement which passed Belgorod and reached Tetervino before being forced to retreat. During the action, it claimed to have destroyed 500 Soviet tanks.

10 forward gears in addition to the single reverse. Weight increased to 20 tons and around 100 Ausf. Es were made in 1939.

Construction of the Ausf. F, regarded as the first full production model of the Panzer III, also began in 1939. Initially it was similar in most respects to the Ausf. E, except for new brake ventilation ducts, but late production models were fitted with a new main gun – the 50mm KwK 38 L/42. All existing Ausf. Es were also retrospectively upgraded with the new gun. With the larger ammunition size required, fewer rounds could be carried: 99 for the main gun and 3750 for the machine guns.

A total of 450 Ausf. Fs were produced from 1939 to 1941, with production lines starting to turn out its successor, the Ausf. G in October 1940. The G featured a revised cupola, improved gun mantlet armour, bigger radiators and an additional felt air filter.

By now the Panzer III had seen active service during the invasions of France and Poland and it had become clear that its armour was too thin. Therefore, production of the Ausf. H began with extra 30mm armour plates bolted on to the front and rear hull. In order to carry this additional weight and reduce ground pressure, the H had wider 40cm tracks with new drive sprockets and idlers, plus strengthened torsion bar suspension.

It had also been realised by now that the Maybach Variorex gearbox was too complicated to facilitate easy maintenance so this was replaced with an Aphon synchromesh box with six forward gears and reverse. The Ausf. H weighed 21.6 tons but the vehicle's top speed was unaffected. A total of 286 Ausf. Hs were built.

The most numerous Panzer III was the Ausf. J, construction of which began in 1941. Rather than requiring bolt-on armour, this was factory-built with solid 50mm plate armour. Brake levers replaced the brake pedals of earlier models. While early examples of the J were still fitted with the KwK 38 L/42, this was quickly supplanted by the longer-barrelled KwK 39 L/60 gun. Ammunition load was correspondingly reduced to 78 rounds. Between the end of 1941 and the middle of 1942 a total of 1521 Ausf. Js were constructed.

Combat experience soon demonstrated that even the 50mm plate was wholly inadequate against the latest Allied and Soviet anti-tank guns but adding yet more bolt-on plates would have put too much strain on the vehicle's drive train and suspension so a different approach was needed. Some creative thinking resulted in the Ausf. L. This had a system of spaced armour – with 20mm ▶

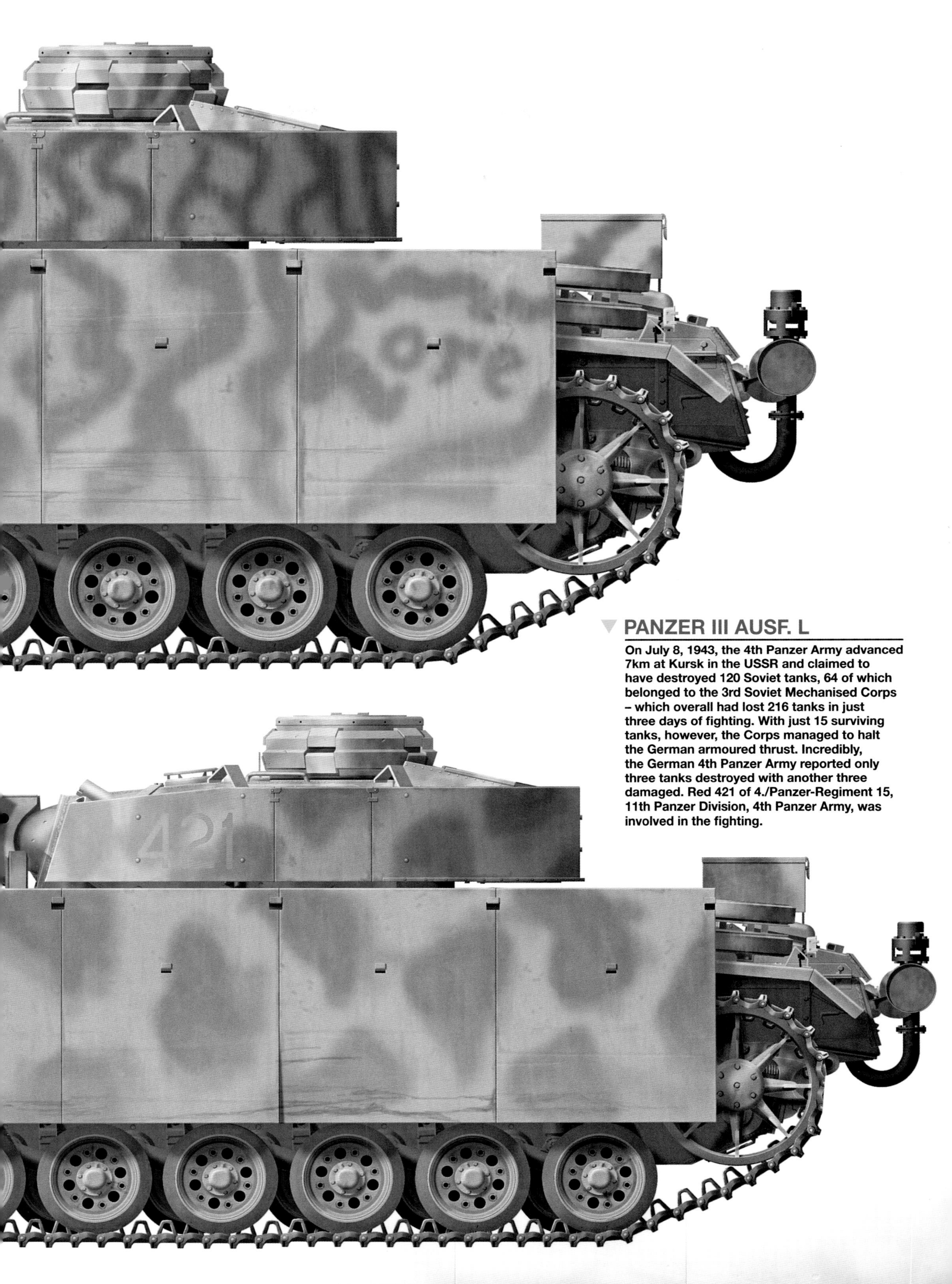

PANZER III AUSF. L

On July 8, 1943, the 4th Panzer Army advanced 7km at Kursk in the USSR and claimed to have destroyed 120 Soviet tanks, 64 of which belonged to the 3rd Soviet Mechanised Corps – which overall had lost 216 tanks in just three days of fighting. With just 15 surviving tanks, however, the Corps managed to halt the German armoured thrust. Incredibly, the German 4th Panzer Army reported only three tanks destroyed with another three damaged. Red 421 of 4./Panzer-Regiment 15, 11th Panzer Division, 4th Panzer Army, was involved in the fighting.

PANZERKAMPFWAGEN III

PANZER III AUSF. L ▶

Black 234, an early Ausf. L retrofitted with hull and turret spaced armour, belonged to 2./Panzer-Regiment 33, 'Prinz Eugen', 9th Panzer Division. Note the lack of additional armour on the hull front and turret mantle. It was probably lost during heavy combat at the Battle of the Dnieper, USSR, January 1944. The photo upon which this profile is based shows the seemingly intact but immobilised tank being examined by Red Army soldiers. During these battles the regiment suffered mounting losses and by January 1944 was reduced to just 13 tanks. The battle of the Dnieper Bend lasted from January 1 to March 29. In April the exhausted regiment was pulled out of the fighting, its vehicles loaded on to railway carriages and sent to France for rest and refit.

metal plates being fitted slightly ahead of the front plate and mantlet. Nevertheless, the vehicle's weight continued to rise, reaching 22.3 tons. Some 1470 examples were built.

Similar in appearance to the L, the Ausf. M differed in having a self-sealing exhaust which allowed it to wade through rivers and other bodies of water up to a depth of 1.5m. Six smoke-bomb launchers, three on either side of the turret, were also fitted.

The last production version, the Ausf. N, saw the Panzer III and Panzer IV swap roles. While the former support vehicle was upgraded to become a main battle tank, the Panzer III became an infantry support vehicle fitted with the same 75mm KwK 37 L/24 gun that had originally seen service on the Panzer IV. The N carried 64 rounds of ammunition for attacking fixed positions and providing fire support against enemy infantry.

By the summer of 1943 it had long been clear that the Panzer III's chassis could no longer accept further upgrades as a turreted tank – though it continued to be manufactured as the basis of the StuG III assault gun. Production of the Panzer III ceased in August 1943 though examples lingered on in front-line service up to the end of 1944. By this time, these vehicles had been coated with Zimmerit anti-magnetic mine paste and had both spaced turret shrouds and side skirts fitted to defend against hollow charges fired by enemy infantry at close range.

A variety of different post-production Panzer III conversions were made, including 100 examples of the PzKpfw III (Flam) based on the Ausf. M – which had a flame projector tube fitted in place of the tank's main gun. The tank carried 100 litres of highly flammable liquid internally which was pumped through the tube using a small two-stroke motor. Just three men crewed these vehicles – the commander doubling as the gunner, with a driver and a radio operator.

The most common conversion, based on Ausf. D, E, H or L chassis,

PANZER III AUSF. J ▲

The Red Army had planned to begin a counter-offensive against the invading German armies on July 9, 1943, but found itself instead facing another early morning German offensive. Black 511 of 5./Panzer-Regiment 15, 11th Panzer Division, 4th Panzer Army, was involved in the attack near Kursk. The Russians had 1800 tanks and the Germans just 670 but nevertheless the 11th Panzer Division made significant progress and managed to achieve its objectives with support from the Luftwaffe. The Soviets lost 5000 men and 60 tanks, compared to German losses of 800 men and two tanks. Overall, however, 1943 saw a decline in the number of German divisions on the Eastern Front from 214 to 190, many of them under-strength, while the Soviets increased their fighting force from 442 divisions to 512.

was to create Panzerbefehlswagens or 'command tanks'. These featured a fixed turret with a dummy gun and a loop aerial positioned over the engine deck. Each vehicle had four radio sets – two at the front of the fighting compartment and two to the rear.

Conversions of Panzer IIIs into Panzerbeobachtungswagen or 'observation tanks' began in 1943. These had their main gun replaced with a single centrally mounted machine gun and contained equipment linking the tank directly to artillery positions to the rear. ●

PANZER III AUSF. L

Black 001 'Brigitte' was a Panzerbefehlswagen of Stab/Panzer-Artillerie-Regiment 103. It is depicted here as it appeared while stationed at Preekule in Latvia during October 1944, under the command of Major Ingfried Hintze. At this time, what remained of the unit was part of the 4th Panzer Division, itself part of Army Group North alongside the 11th SS Volunteer Panzergrenadier Division 'Nordland' and the 30th Infantry Division, and was trapped inside the area known as the Courland Pocket. Hintze's unit had 35 field guns remaining out of 45 by early November but only 56 rounds of ammunition for each one. After months of bitter fighting, the unit was evacuated to Germany by sea to continue the fight. Hintze survived the war and ended up joining the West German Bundeswehr, retiring as a colonel.

PANZER IV

Designed to provide support for the Panzer III by knocking out fixed emplacements and strongpoints, the Panzer IV proved to be a remarkably durable and capable vehicle – ensuring a front-line career which lasted throughout the war.

The specification that would lead to the Panzerkampfwagen IV was issued by Oberst Guderian on January 11, 1934 – the same day as the spec drafted for what would become the Panzer III. As previously mentioned the two machines were intended to work in tandem, with the Panzer III destroying enemy tanks with its armour-piercing 37mm rounds and the Panzer IV destroying static positions with its 75mm KwK 37 L/24 howitzer.

Three firms tendered for the specification and built prototype machines: Krupp, MAN and Rheinmetall-Borsig. Krupp's design, which featured interleaved six-wheel suspension, was chosen for further development and it was proposed that it should be fitted with torsion bar suspension instead. However, due to time pressure, Krupp opted for a leaf spring double-bogie suspension instead. The resulting vehicle had eight small rubber-rimmed roadwheels on each side which were suspended in pairs from the leaf spring units. Four return rollers were required in addition to the usual

1936-1945

drive sprocket and rear idler wheel. Track width was 380mm.

The internal layout of the Panzer IV was very similar to that of the Panzer III. The 250hp Maybach 108TR engine was mounted to the rear of the vehicle and the five-speed manual with one reverse speed transmission was up front, with the final drive running across the front of the vehicle to the drive sprocket on either side. Top speed was 30km/h. As with the Panzer III, the driver sat on the left of the transmission and the radio operator/ hull gunner on the right. The commander sat in the centre beneath his cupola, the gunner was on the left of the gun breech and the loader was on the right.

The engine was offset 152.4mm to the right of the vehicles' centreline and the turret was offset 66.5mm to the left, allowing the shaft which connected the engine with the transmission to avoid the rotary base junction unit which supplied electrical power to the turret. On the left of the engine compartment was a two-stroke auxiliary generator which kept the vehicle's batteries charged without putting additional strain on the engine.

The first version of the Panzer IV, the Ausf. A, had a single 7.92mm machine gun mounted coaxially in its turret alongside the 75mm howitzer and another 7.92mm mounted in the front of the hull. At the rear of the turret was the simple commander's cupola with a two-piece hatch and on the turret sides were one-piece hatches. Maximum armour thickness on the chassis was just 14.5mm, with the turret offering slightly thicker 20mm armour. A total of 35 were built.

Production of the Ausf. B commenced in 1937. The biggest change was the ▶

PANZER IV AUSF. F2 (G)

During August 1942, the Panzer IV Ausf. F2 (G) was capable of knocking out any British or American tank at ranges up to 2000m with its 75mm L/43 gun. Feld Marschall Erwin Rommel had 27 of them available during the Battle of Alam el Halfa pass, south of El Alamein, from August 30 to September 5. This particular example is Red 843 of the 21st Panzer Division as it appeared on August 31, 1942. For the first stage of the battle, the Panzer IV Ausf. F2 (G)s were placed at the front of the assault, engaging British tanks at long range. Then the 21st Panzer Division turned north to face 22nd Armoured Brigade's mixed force of Grants and Crusaders. Having created a gap in the British lines by knocking out a dozen of these, despite some casualties, the Germans rushed forward. However, they met concentrated enemy fire particularly from the surrounding hills and were forced to withdraw to their original positions. This was Rommel's last major offensive in the Western Desert.

PANZER IV

PANZER IV AUSF. F2 (G)

White 613 of Panzer-Regiment 29, 12th Panzer Division, 18th Army, seen here at Volkhov, USSR in September 1942, was a very early production vehicle finished in overall RAL 7021 Dunkelgrau. The 12th had been sent to Estonia for a rest and refit after suffering heavy casualties in the Soviet offensive during the winter of 1941-42 but returned to action during the spring of 1942. Here it acted as a tactical reserve for the Army Group North, going wherever armoured support was needed and fighting battles at Volkhov, Lake Ladoga and Nevel. It was then involved in the Siege of Leningrad, where its tanks were instrumental in the destruction of the Soviet 8th and 2nd Shock Armies. The division was transferred to Army Group Centre in November 1942.

engine, with the Panzer IV now receiving the 300hp Maybach HL 120TR engine – which the Panzer III had to wait until 1939 for – and a new six-speed gearbox. The glacis plate of the tank was straightened and up-armoured to 30mm with a new driver's vision slit included but with the hull machine gun deleted. Some Ausf. Bs received a better turret cupola, adopted from the Panzer III Ausf. C with latches for the vision slits. The vehicle weighed 16.1 tons and speed was increased to 42km/h. A total of 42 were built.

The Panzer IV Ausf. C was introduced in 1938. This had 30mm turret armour and the slightly improved Maybach HL 120TRM engine was introduced to the production line after the first 30 vehicles out of a total of 140 built up to August 1939. Weight was 18.14 tons.

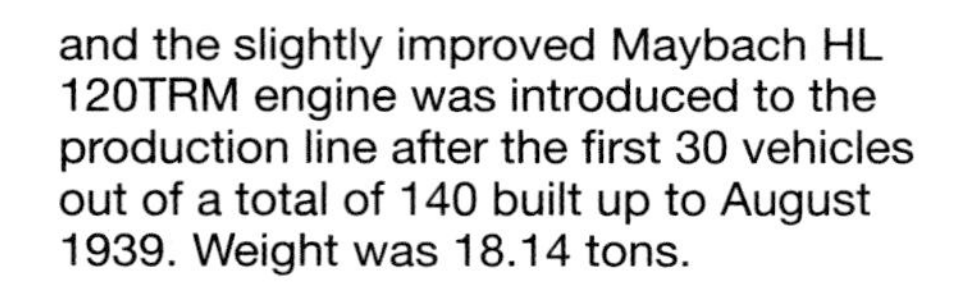

The hull-mounted machine gun was reintroduced for the Ausf. D and the turret gun received a new turret mantlet with 35mm armour. Side armour was also increased in thickness to 20mm. Ausf. D production ran for 248 vehicles before the next major improvement.

The Ausf. E's bow plate armour was increased to 30mm while an additional steel plate was added to the glacis, giving it a total of 60mm thickness. The driver's position got a new visor and the commander's cupola from the Panzer III Ausf. G was adopted. Between October 1940 and April 1941 a total of 206 Panzer IV Ausf. Es were built.

Construction of the Ausf. F then commenced. This had 50mm armour on the hull front and turret, with the side armour increasing in thickness once again to 30mm – overall weight rising correspondingly to 22.3 tons. This resulted in an unwelcome increase in ground pressure so track width had to be increased to 400mm with the sprockets and idlers being modified to suit. An auxiliary generator muffler was mounted to the left of the main engine exhaust and the latter was shortened. With the invasion of the Soviet Union in June 1941, the number of German tanks required increased dramatically, so 471 Ausf. Fs ▶

◀ PANZER IV AUSF. G

After being defeated at the Battle of Faïd Pass and Sidi Bouzid on February 17, 1943, American forces fell back to the Kasserine Pass in western Tunisia. On the 19th, Rommel attacked the Allied lines and forced the US troops to retreat. The next day Rommel personally led a battle-group of the German 10th Panzer Division in an attack towards the pass. The inexperienced American troops broke within minutes. Black 8 is pictured here as it appeared on February 20, 1943. On the offensive's third day the division attacked toward Thala and the Americans continued to fall back, leaving the Axis forces to capture large amounts of heavy equipment. On February 21, the division was positioned outside Thala where the Germans met stronger resistance as experienced British infantry had replaced the Americans on the front line. Finally on the 23rd, Rommel gave the order to withdraw eastward to avoid a British attack from Libya, allowing the Americans to retake the pass. Black 8 was found blown-up when the Axis forces capitulated in May. It is believed that it was painted in overall RAL 7027 Grau, a shade better suited to the scrubbier Tunisian terrain.

PANZER IV

were produced between April 1941 and March 1942.

Reports of encounters with the British Matilda II tank in the Western Desert during December 1940 and January 1941 convinced Adolf Hitler that both the Panzer III and Panzer IV needed improved armament. On February 19, 1941, with Panzer IV Ausf. F production ongoing, he ordered that long 50mm cannon should be fitted to both tanks. Krupp therefore began to design a 50mm KwK L/60 gun and had an example ready to demonstrate to Hitler on his 52nd birthday – April 20, 1941. However, it soon became clear that this gun would still not be powerful enough and plans to manufacture it from August 1941 were cancelled.

Krupp was forced to think again. The company had already produced a potent 75mm L/40 for the StuG but this was too long. Shortening the barrel would give reduced armour-piercing capability however, so Krupp also had to develop a new armour-piercing round in tandem with the gun. The result was the 75mm KwK L/34.5, which was tested in one tank in April 1942.

However, in November 1941 Krupp was ordered to cooperate with Rheinmetall-Borsig in the development of another new gun – the 75mm KwK 40 L/43. Although this new gun allowed the Panzer IV to penetrate 77mm of armour at 1830m, its long barrel increased the strain on the already hard-pushed forward suspension, meaning it was constantly compressed rather than springing back and forth as the tank moved over uneven terrain. Initially the gun was fitted to Ausf. Fs rolling off the production line but after three months this 'F2' was redesignated the Ausf. G. These tanks had a total of 87 main gun rounds and 3150 rounds of belted ammunition for their 7.92mm machine guns.

Built from March 1942 to June 1943, the Ausf. G underwent numerous on-the-run production changes as a total of 994 Fs and Gs were built in 1942. Slits were created in the rear engine ▶

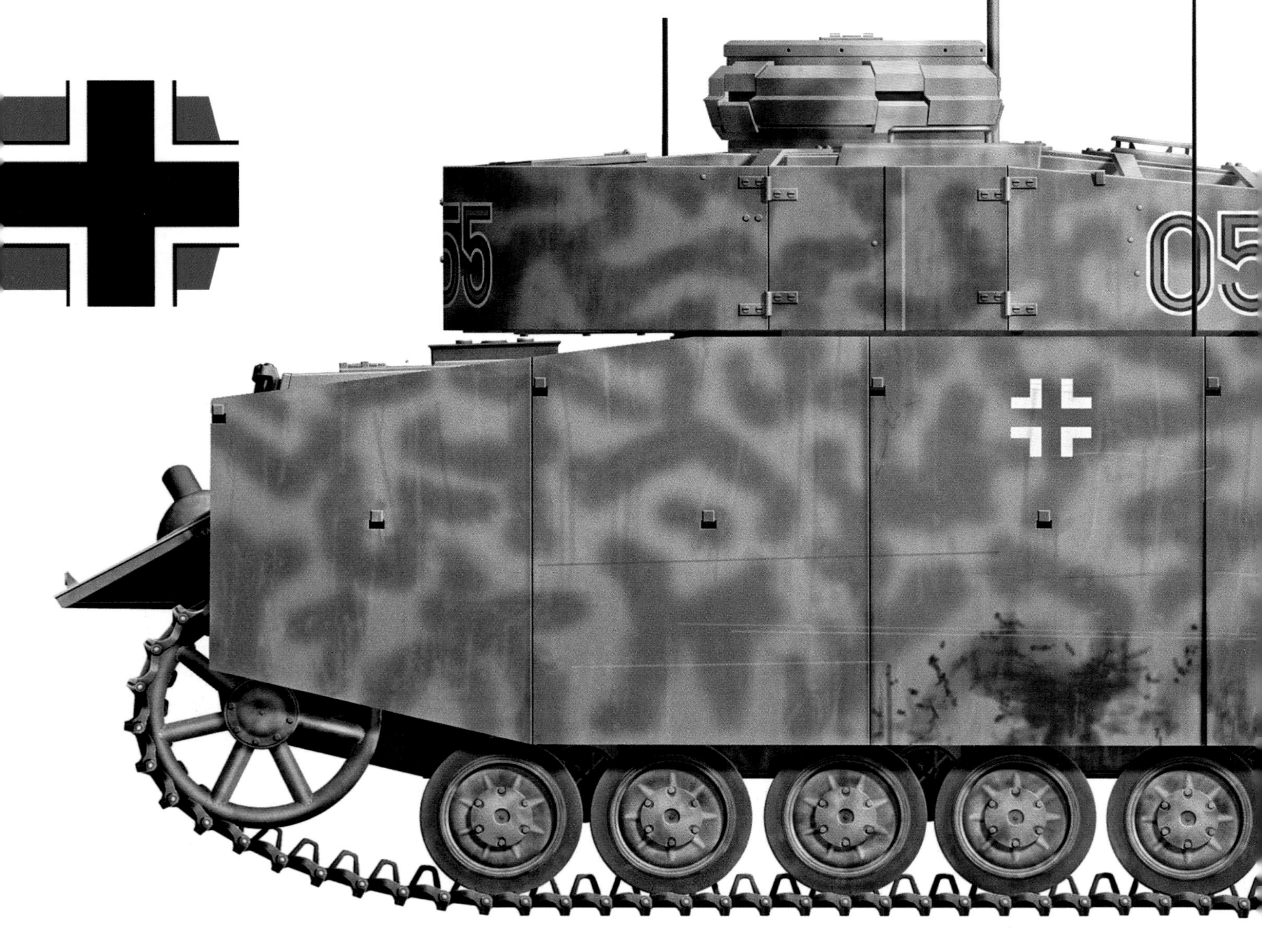

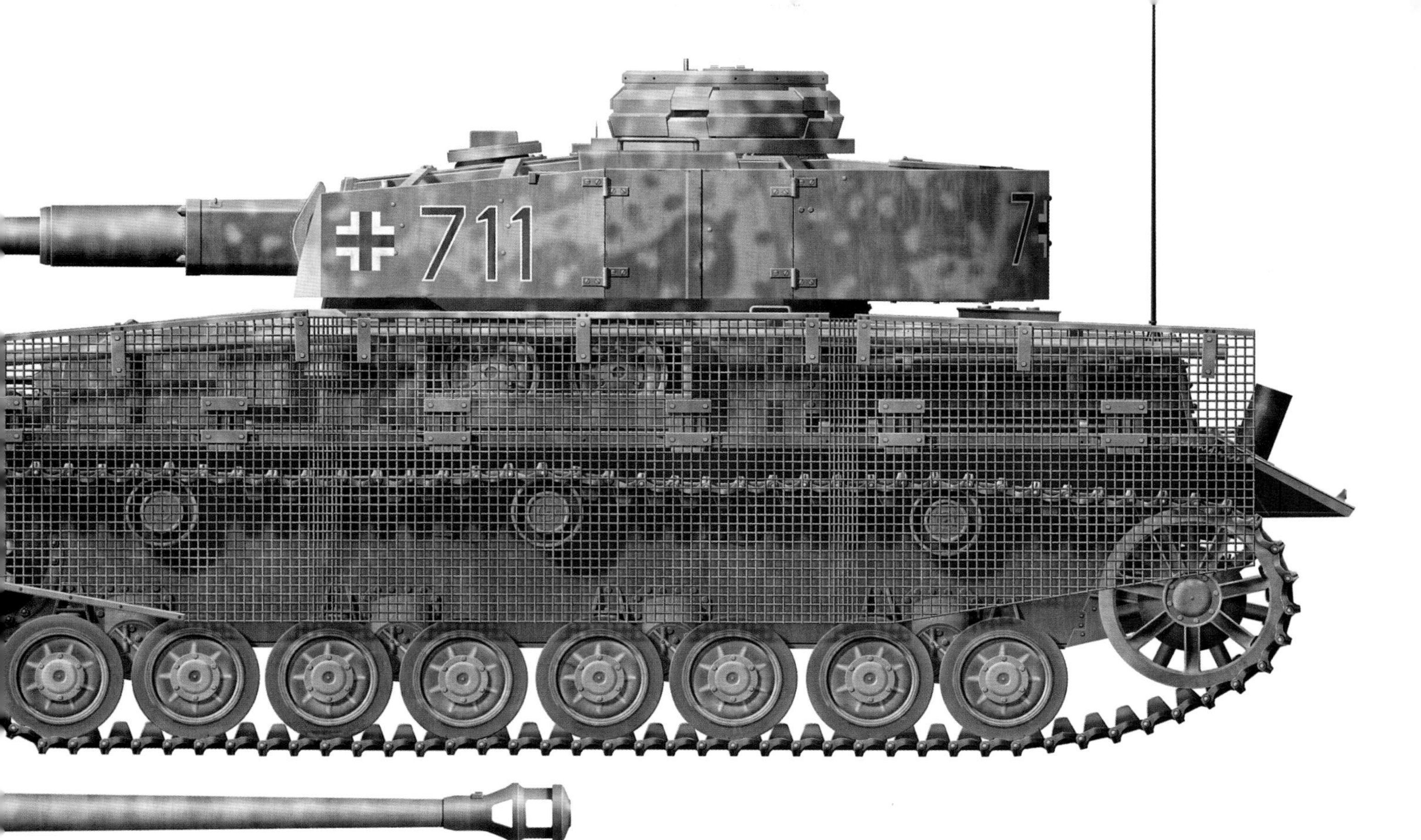

Panzerbefehlswagens or 'command tanks'. These had extra radio sets, mounting racks and other electrical equipment which resulted in the space available for main gun armament being reduced from 87 rounds to 72. Also like the Panzer III, the Panzer IV was sometimes used as the basis for a Panzerbeobachtungswagen or 'observation tank' for artillery spotting. The commander's cupola was replaced with a shorter unit with seven periscopes rather than the standard cupola's five vision slits and additional radio sets were installed along with an artillery plotting board. ●

PANZER IV AUSF. H

White 505 was a Panzerbefehlswagen of II./Panzer-Regiment 29, 12th Panzer Division. This is how it looked at Slagüne in Latvia during late September 1944. The 12th took part in Operation Cäsar on the Eastern Front in late September 1944. This was an attempt to re-form a cohesive front line between Army Groups North and Centre by conducting a second assault. The attack began on September 16 and the Red Army responded with fierce resistance. On the 21st the offensive came to a halt after XXXIX Panzer-Korps only managed to penetrate a few kilometres. The Germans realised that their resources were not sufficient for a renewed offensive and so were forced to shift to the defensive. The Soviets launched a new offensive on October 5, reaching the Baltic Sea five days later, thereby managing to cut off Army Group North in what was later known as the Courland Pocket. Subsequently, Hitler renamed Army Group North as Army Group Courland since he probably realised that it was impossible to restore the land corridor.

STUG III

The Sturmgeschütz III, originally intended as mobile light artillery, became an effective tank-killer and Germany's most-produced armoured fighting vehicle of the war.

While the Panzer IV was meant to engage fixed positions and knock them out in support of the Panzer III, the German Army felt that there remained a need for a mobile artillery piece that could also provide both direct and indirect fire support for infantry units while protecting its crew with armour.

As a result Daimler-Benz, having just brought the successful Panzer III Ausf. A to the point of series production, was handed a contract on June 15, 1936, to create an infantry support vehicle armed with a short-barrelled 75mm artillery piece that would have a 30-degree traverse to either side within a fixed casemate.

It was to have protection against 7.92mm armour-piercing bullets to the sides and rear with the ability to deflect 20mm rounds at the front. It was also to be open-topped for good all-round visibility and lower in height than the average man, making it harder for enemy tanks and anti-tank guns to spot and hit.

STUG III AUSF. G

The original photograph showing this StuG III with its distinctive tall side skirts gives no indication as to the vehicle's unit, nor to the time and place of the image. Nevertheless, it is of interest due to those side plates and for the unusual striped camouflage pattern employed.

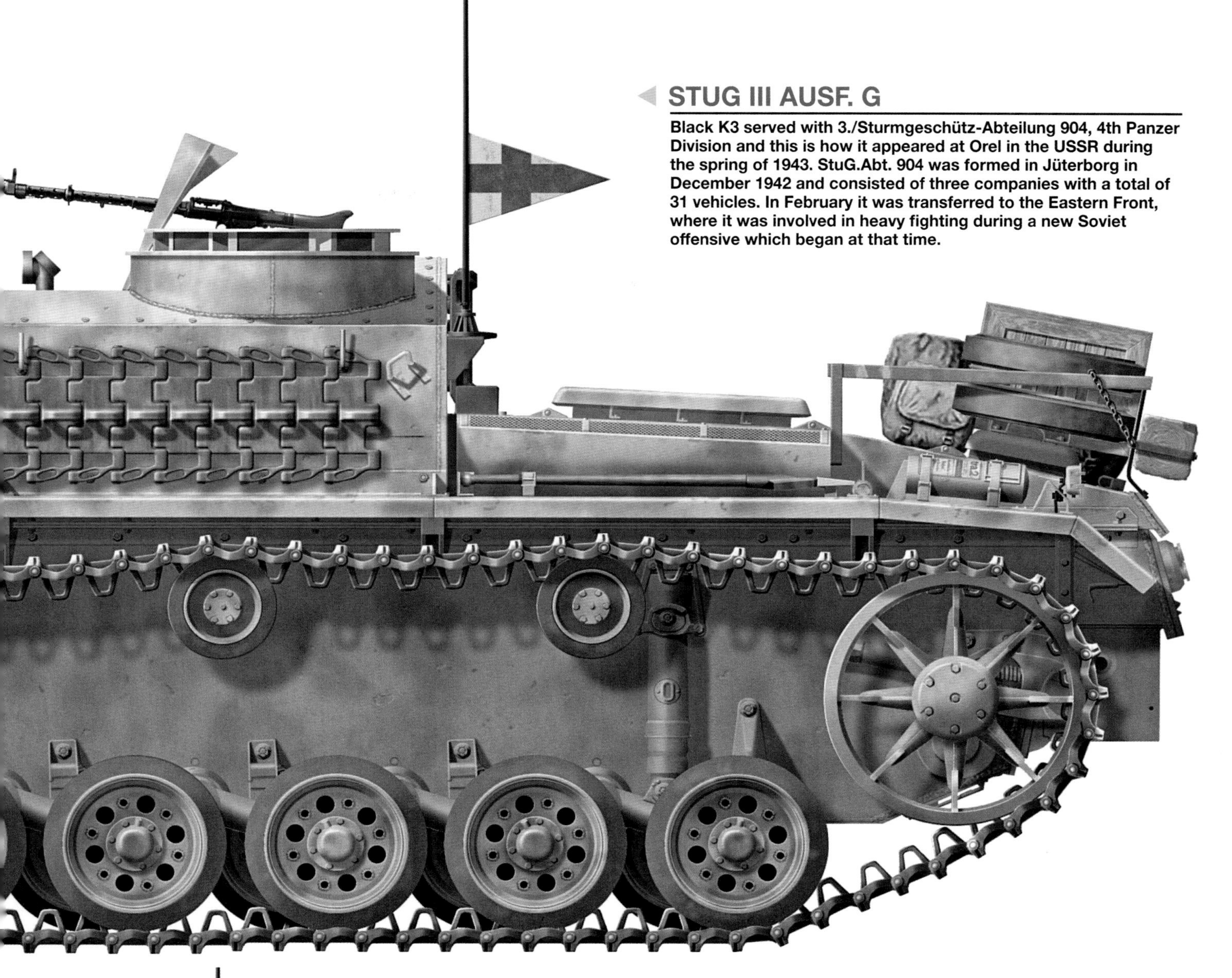

STUG III AUSF. G

Black K3 served with 3./Sturmgeschütz-Abteilung 904, 4th Panzer Division and this is how it appeared at Orel in the USSR during the spring of 1943. StuG.Abt. 904 was formed in Jüterborg in December 1942 and consisted of three companies with a total of 31 vehicles. In February it was transferred to the Eastern Front, where it was involved in heavy fighting during a new Soviet offensive which began at that time.

Daimler-Benz designed the new vehicle using the most advanced Panzer III running gear and underpinnings – those of the Ausf. B – before handing the project over to a subcontractor, Alkett, to build the first five prototypes in 1937.

Krupp was contracted to design the new vehicle's 75mm gun, five examples of which were made and delivered in 1938. In August that year, Krupp was also contracted to design a new long-barrelled 75mm gun for Waffen Prüfamt 4, the section of the Waffenamt responsible for artillery design.

With the five prototype vehicles completed and undergoing trials, a decision was made in 1939 to change the design and make it fully enclosed – protecting the low-down crew from being fired on by enemy infantry when travelling over uneven terrain and particularly when going down slopes. In December 1939, Krupp sent a wooden model of the new long-barrelled gun to Daimler-Benz so that work could begin on determining how best to fit it to the new vehicle in place of the short-barrelled piece.

Named 'Sturmgeschutz' (in practice often shortened to 'StuG' or 'StuG III') on March 28, 1940, the full production vehicle would again be based on the latest version of the Panzer III, now the Ausf. E. All-new components included the armoured hull, a well-sprung height-adjustable driver's seat, track brakes, track ventilation and hydraulic steering. ▶

STUG III

STUG III AUSF. G

This vehicle, Red 100, was used by 1./Panzer-Abteilung 'Rhodos', based at Rhodes, Greece, in November 1943. Sturmdivision 'Rhodos', commanded by Generalleutnant Ulrich Kleemann, consisted of a cadre of officers and NCOs commanding second-rate garrison personnel and political prisoners, some of whom were recruited from concentration camps. Their first baptism of fire came on September 8, 1943, when the Italian garrison on the island tried to negotiate their surrender to the British. Kleemann ordered an attack on 40,000 Italians, defeating them after a series of battles for the loss of 66 Germans killed. The division later took part in the battles for the islands of Corfu, Simi, Rodi, and a few other small Aegean islands. Transport was made possible by the division's own navy of small ships and sailing boats crewed by Greek and Italian volunteers. The last action for the division during the war was a raid against the Turks on March 1, 1945.

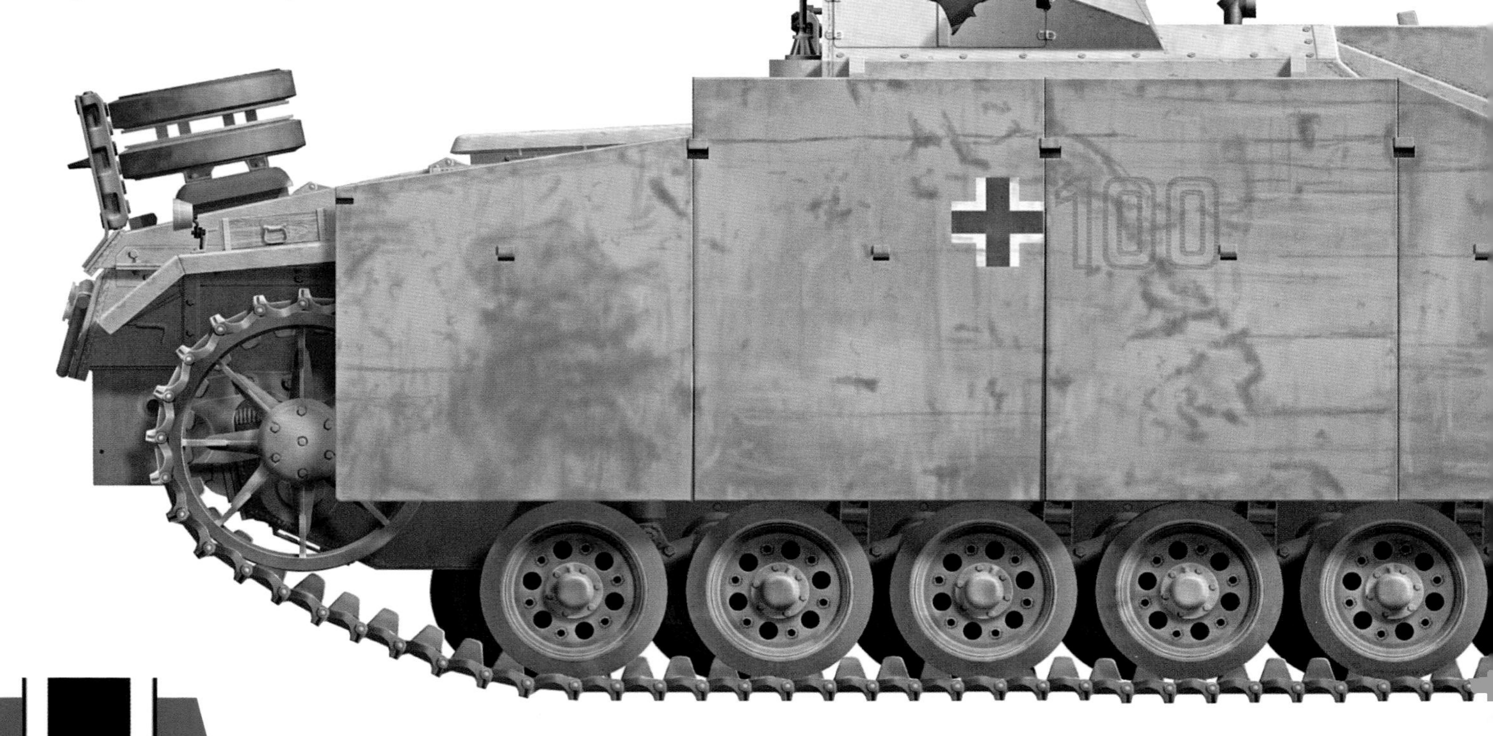

The remainder of the vehicle's parts were simply lifted directly from the Panzer III Ausf. E, the engine being the usual Maybach 120 TRM V12. Top speed was 40km/h but cruising speed when travelling by road was more like 20km/h. On-road range was 155km and 95km off-road.

Armour thickness at the front was 50mm with 30mm to the sides and rear. There was a crew of four – commander, driver, gunner and loader. The driver could see out of a slot in the front plate, another slot to his left or through twin periscopes, the gunner could only see out through the periscopic gun sight, the commander got a scissors periscope and the loader was completely without external visibility.

The driver's escape hatch was the steering brake inspection hatch but each of the others had a hatch directly above his head.

The StuG's 75mm L/24 cannon, adapted from the KwK L/24 carried by the Panzer IV, was mounted on a sturdy frame and had to be elevated and traversed by hand. It could be moved up 20 degrees from centre, down 10 degrees and left and right just 12 degrees either way. Thirty-two rounds for the main gun were stowed away in metal bins with hinged lids in front of the loader, while another dozen were kept in another bin at the back of the crew compartment.

NAMED 'STURMGESCHUTZ' (IN PRACTICE OFTEN SHORTENED TO 'STUG' OR 'STUG III') ON MARCH 28, 1940, THE FULL PRODUCTION VEHICLE WOULD AGAIN BE BASED ON THE LATEST VERSION OF THE PANZER III, NOW THE AUSF. E.

The vehicle had no other weapon so the crew themselves were equipped with a pair of machine pistols, 12 stick grenades and five smoke grenades. The machine pistols had 192 rounds of ammunition each. Just one radio set was fitted to the StuG and the commander operated it. There was no crew intercom – just a loudspeaker by which the commander could relay his orders to the gun crew and a simple speaking tube linking the commander and the driver. The StuG Ausf. A weighed 20.7 tons and just 30 of them were made.

The StuG Ausf. B incorporated the mechanical improvements featured in the Panzer III Ausf. H including wider tracks, improved steering and ventilation for the brakes. On the outside, the Ausf. B received new track guards, exhaust mufflers and rear fender flaps. Two hundred and fifty were made.

The Ausf. C saw only minor changes, with a new periscopic gunsight being added and the seals around the steering brake access hatches being altered. Just 50 examples were produced. The Ausf. D had hardened frontal armour but otherwise the only difference was the installation of an electric bell so that the commander could attract the driver's attention – the speaking tube being insufficient on its own. A total of 150 were built.

On the Ausf. E's external superstructure, the armoured pannier on the left-hand side was made longer and a new pannier was added on the right. This allowed for the installation of additional radio equipment, with a FuG 16 being used by the loader. The pannier on the ▶

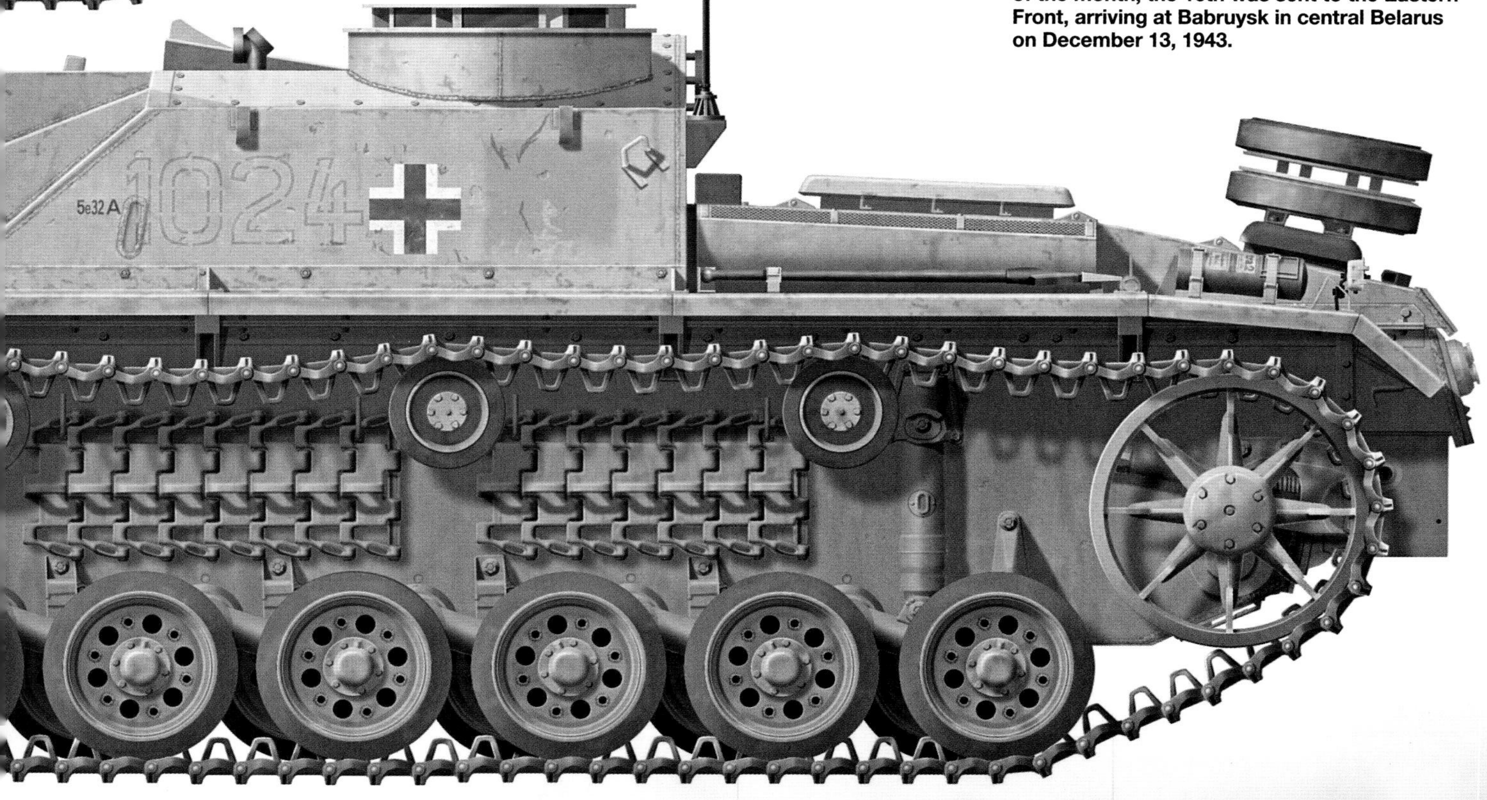

STUG III AUSF. G

The 16th Panzer Division staged a fighting withdrawal towards Rome and the Siegfried Line during October 1943. The division enjoyed a brief period of respite during early November and that is the point at which Red 1024 is depicted, the original photograph showing it close to the Piazza del Popolo in Rome. The number comes from it being the 4th vehicle of the 2nd platoon of the 10th company. The vehicle belonged to the 16th's III./Abteilung, 10./Panzer-Regiment 2. During the latter part of the month, the 16th was sent to the Eastern Front, arriving at Babruysk in central Belarus on December 13, 1943.

STUG III

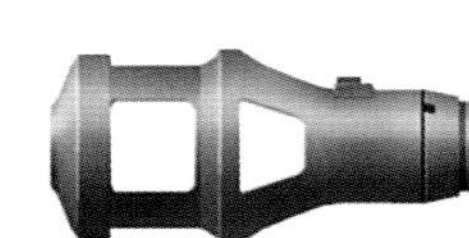

STUG III AUSF. G

Black 232 of 2./Panzerjäger-Abteilung 243, 243. Infanterie-Division, was based at Cherbourg, Normandy, France, during late June 1944. Note the squared pattern on the Zimmerit paste applied to this vehicle, looking much like the familiar waffle pattern. The 243rd's heavy equipment tended to be obsolete or captured Czech, French and Russian weapons, even though the crews were actually battle-hardened veterans of the Eastern Front. It was deployed to the north of the Cotentin Peninsula and was under constant attack immediately after the D-Day landings. Later withdrawn to 'Fortress Cherbourg', the division suffered crippling losses and was almost entirely destroyed in the fighting at Saint-Lô. It was formally disbanded on September 12, 1944.

left also allowed an extra six rounds to be carried for the main gun. While an order for 500 was placed, just 284 examples were actually built.

By now, the long-barrelled gun originally developed for the StuG by Krupp had been superseded by an improved model designed by Rheinmetall-Borsig – the 75mm Stu.K.40 L/43. This fired the new Pzgr.39 shell which had been aerodynamically designed to achieve higher speeds and therefore had a greater chance of penetrating enemy armour.

The first StuG fitted with the new gun, the Ausf. F, entered production in March 1942. The front of the superstructure was significantly modified to allow sufficient space for the new weapon with its more substantial recoil and recuperator cylinders. Also, a roof-mounted exhaust fan was fitted. Stowage was increased part way through the F's production run so that 56 rounds could now be carried for the main gun.

In addition to the gun itself, the Ausf. F's crew received a single MG 34 with 600 rounds of ammunition to supplement their two machine pistols and 12 stick grenades. After 121 Ausf. Fs had been produced, the Stu.K.40 L/43 was replaced with the even longer L/48. In addition, extra 30mm armour plates were welded on to the front of the hull beginning in June 1942. The overall weight of the vehicle had steadily crept up and now reached 21.6 tons.

Next came the interim type Ausf. F/8. This adopted the hull design of the Panzer III Ausf. J, with extended sides, different brake access hatches and a new rear deck which provided better cooling for the engine below. From December 1942, the Ausf. F/8 was fitted with a small shield on the roof positioned in front of the loader's hatch to provide him with cover when he was using the vehicle's MG 34.

Around 700 Ausf. Fs and F/8s were built from March to December 1942, when production switched to the final

STUG III AUSF. G

Belonging to the 9. SS Panzer Division 'Hohenstaufen', this StuG III was at Longchamps, Belgium, on January 3-4, 1945, during some of the fiercest fighting of the Ardennes campaign. The US 101st Airborne Division launched an attack against the Germans north of Bastogne on January 3 but were met by intensive artillery fire, forcing them back to their original positions. The 'Hohenstaufen' then attacked the 101st from the north and managed to capture the villages of Longchamps and Monaville. The attack continued on the 4th and resulted in a panicked withdrawal of US forces and high casualties among the American forces. General George Patton wrote in his diary: "The German freezes more than us and they are hungrier than we are, but they fight better."

distinct variant of the StuG III – the Ausf. G. This featured a redesigned superstructure with a seven-periscope cupola for the commander, extended sides and a repositioned fan to improve the extraction of fumes from the gun breech. The gunner's hatch was also deleted.

STUG III

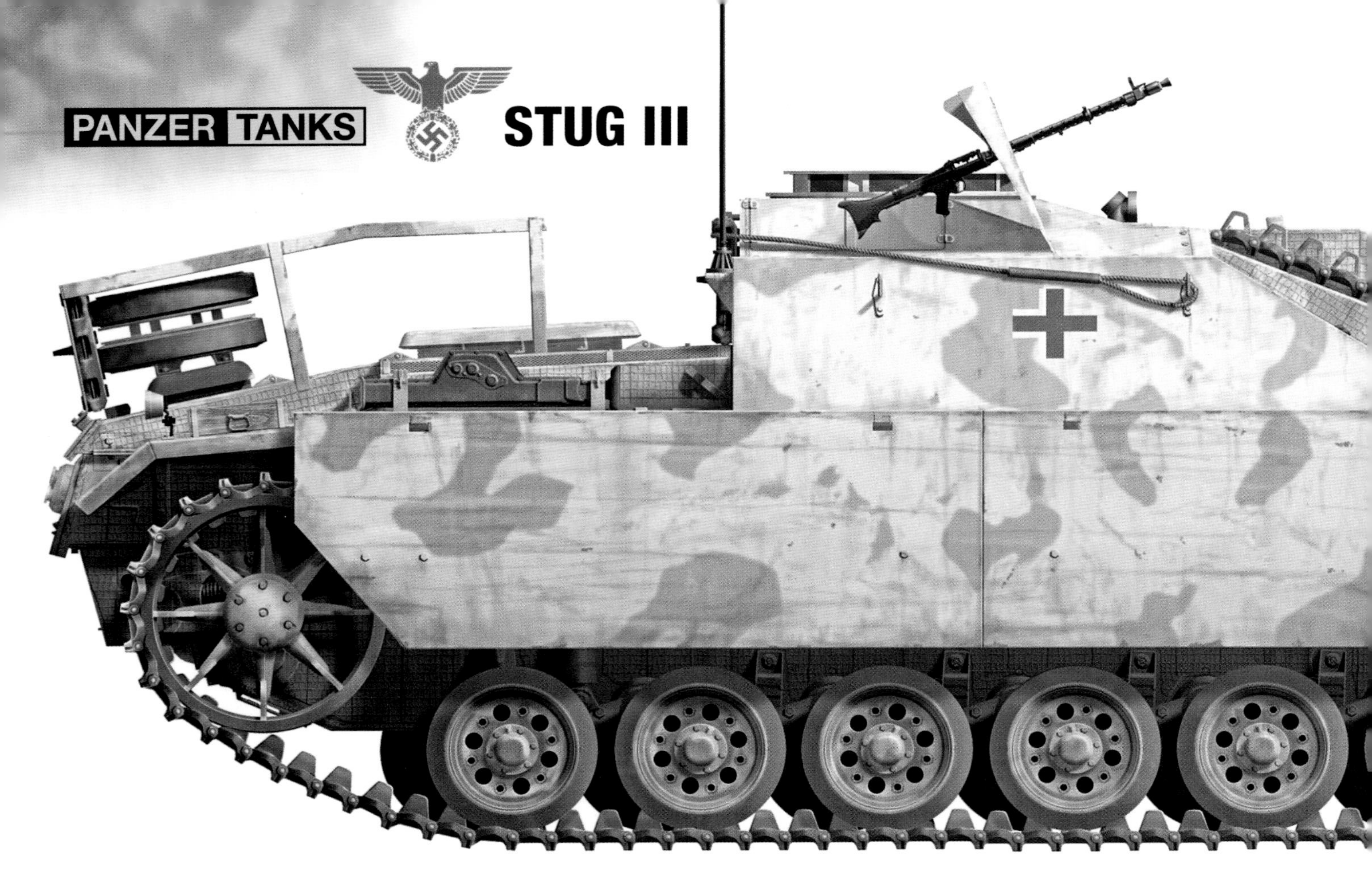

Early on in the G's production run, the driver's side vision slot was replaced with a pistol port and the armour plates on the side panniers were fitted at a sharper angle to increase protection. In January 1943, the breech fume extractor fan was moved again, this time to the rear wall of the fighting compartment.

The driver's twin periscope was deleted in February 1943 and the holes left were plugged up. Spaced armour side skirts were fitted from April 1943 and from May 1943 the vehicle's frontal armour was cast as a single 80mm thick plate rather than being cast as a 50mm plate and having the additional 30mm of armour bolted on. Just like every other German armoured fighting vehicle, from September 1943 Zimmerit paste was applied to StuG IIIs to prevent the enemy from attaching magnetic mines. A cast gun mantle was introduced to some but not all StuG production lines from November 1943, replacing the old armour-plate mantle.

Four months later, in March 1944, a new remote-controlled machine gun mount was fitted in place of the loader's gun shield on the vehicle's roof. The MG 34 could be installed in the mount then fired by the loader from inside the vehicle using a periscope which offered magnification to the power of three and an eight-degree field of vision. Unfortunately, the MG 34 was magazine rather than belt-fed so once the gun ran out of ammunition, the loader would have to open his hatch to change the magazine.

Sockets were welded to the roof of the superstructure from July 1944 so that a two-ton jib boom could be fitted to the vehicle for lifting out components – particularly the engine – when this was necessary. And two months later the application of Zimmerit ceased.

A small number of StuG IIIs were equipped to perform the command vehicle role with long-range radio sets and large aerials mounted on the rear of the superstructure.

Another major variant of the StuG was the Sturmhaubitze. This was fitted with a 105mm light field howitzer for destroying hardened and well dug-in enemy positions such as bunkers. The gun could be traversed 10 degrees to either side and 20 degrees up. Thirty-six rounds could be carried. The first nine prototype examples were completed in October 1942 with

STUG III AUSF. G

'Chery', probably of the 3rd or 5th SS Panzer Division, IV. SS Panzer Korps, as it appeared at Székesfehérvár, Hungary, on January 17, 1945. On this day, the Germans made their third attempt to relieve the besieged city of Budapest with Operation Konrad III. Within the city, 95,000 German and Hungarian troops were trapped together with 800,000 civilians. Attacking from the south, this offensive aimed to encircle 10 Red Army divisions. The effort failed, despite tearing a 24-kilometre hole in the Soviet lines. Finally, on February 13, 1945, the remaining defenders in the city surrendered, costing the Germans and the Hungarians 40,000 dead and 62,000 wounded while the Red Army losses amounted to 82,000 dead and 240,000 wounded. Hitler's decision to undertake offensive actions in both the Ardennes and Hungary resulted in Poland, and thereby the road to Berlin, being left virtually undefended when Stalin launched his winter offensive on January 15.

three more following in November. The production series began in March 1943 and some 1300 had been built by the end of the war.

Although early versions of the StuG III were not built in huge numbers, the vehicle came into its own on the Eastern Front as the war progressed. At the beginning of the summer in 1942 there were 210 StuG IIIs fighting the Soviets, but by the end of November that year, this had increased to 448.

With its powerful long-barrelled 75mm gun, the StuG was just as effective against tanks such as the T-34, T-60 and T-70 as it was against enemy infantry positions. By the start of Operation Citadel against the Russian defences around Kursk at the end of June 1943, there were 26 StuG units operating a total of 727 vehicles.

The Germans increasingly found that the StuG had some clear advantages over tanks such as the Panzer IV – in particular, its low height meant it was harder to hit and easier to conceal. Its frontal armour was adequate and its mobility was on a par with that of turreted tanks. Complaints about the StuG included the lack of an anti-infantry machine gun that could be fired from inside the vehicle, the need to repeatedly shift the whole vehicle's position in order to aim the gun – putting pressure on the steering and brakes – and the weak 30mm side armour.

Between January and August 1944, StuG units claimed a total of 4667 Soviet tanks destroyed for a loss of 713 StuG IIIs – an incredible kill ratio, even allowing for over-reporting. It has been estimated that by the end of the war, StuGs had knocked out some 35,000 Allied tanks overall.

A total of 10,086 StuG IIIs were built, not including the 1300 Sturmhaubitzes. ●

STUG III AUSF. G

Arriving at the port of Libau, Latvia, on January 15 by sea after the Courland Peninsula was cut off by the Red Army in mid-October 1944, Heeres-Sturmartillerie Brigade 600 was equipped with 19 brand new StuG IIIs and 12 Sturmhaubitzes. Among these was White 131. The unit also had a pair of T-34 chassis that had been fitted out as recovery vehicles. The brigade was eventually dissolved on April 12 and its remaining 11 StuGs were incorporated into other units.

1942-1945

TIGER I

Just the sight of a Tiger was usually enough to strike fear into the hearts of enemy tank crews. With thick armour and a powerful 88mm gun, it was capable of defeating anything that crossed its path. Though by no means invincible, it was a formidable fighting machine.

Germany would win its greatest tactical successes during the first year of the war using relatively fast and agile small and medium tanks but as early as January 1937 the Heeres Waffenamt, the German Army armaments department, had awarded Henschel a contract to begin development of a much larger tank.

This was to be a Durchbruchwagen or 'breakthrough vehicle' weighing between 30 and 33 tons. A single turretless prototype known as the DW 1

TIGER I AUSF. H ▲

The 502nd Heavy Panzer Battalion suffered heavy losses of Tiger Is and Panzer IIIs during the Soviet encirclement of Schlüsselburg, east of Leningrad, on January 16, 1943, and the subsequent German break-out attempt. A total of five Tiger Is were lost in the break-out on the 18th. By early February, the unit had only five operational Tigers, including Black 4. It continued to fight in the first battle of Ladoga, however, with a small number of Tigers and Panzer IIIs repelling the Soviet offensive. Its claims during this month amounted to 107 Soviet tanks. In all, it destroyed more than 1400 tanks and 2000 anti-tank guns during its existence for the loss of 88 Tigers in combat.

was built but this went no further because while it was under construction the specification was changed to require thicker armour. Again, Henschel was contracted to produce a vehicle to the revised specification, resulting in one prototype DW 2, but again the Army's requirements changed.

While this work was ongoing, Henschel had also constructed a far heavier tank designated VK 65.01. The VK stood for VollKette or 'fully tracked', with the first two digits of the number denoting the vehicle's weight in tons and the last two being the number of the prototype in that weight category. This was designed to have 100mm of frontal armour with 80mm on the sides. Its gun was to be a short-barrelled 75mm cannon.

In 1939, the Waffenamt put forward another set of specifications and this time Henschel faced competition from three other companies for the contract – MAN, Daimler-Benz and Porsche. Designs were drawn up and on September 9, 1939, Henschel duly received another contract, this time for four prototypes designed VK 30.01 (H), with the 'H' standing for Henschel, using a number of components previously developed for the DW 2.

The company was also contracted to build six prototypes of a 36-ton design, the VK 36.01 (H). Both were to be fitted with a torsion bar suspension system featuring overlapping and interleaved road wheels that was already commonly used for German half-track vehicles.

During the Battle of France in 1940, the German Army's fast but lightweight Panzer IIs and medium Panzer IIIs ▶

TIGER I

TIGER I AUSF. H ▶

Red 731 aka 'Norbert' of the 501st Heavy Panzer Battalion's 7th Company as it appeared at the end of February 1943 at Beja in Tunisia. Up until February 26, Norbert had been part of the 1st Heavy Panzer Regiment, where it had worn turret number 131.

came up against heavily armoured French Char B1 and British Matilda II tanks and it became clear to Adolf Hitler that a heavier tank with more firepower was urgently required. He felt that the Waffenamt was progressing too slowly with Henschel and therefore independently awarded a contract for the design of a 45-ton tank to Henschel's competitor Porsche during the autumn of 1940.

Porsche's owner Dr Ferdinand Porsche was a personal friend of Hitler, having produced the Volkswagen 'people's car', later known as the Beetle, for him two years earlier in 1938. He was also convinced that heavier tanks were needed but believed that a conventional mechanical drivetrain would be too weak. He therefore came up with a complex electro-mechanical system where two air-cooled 320hp 10-cylinder Porsche 101 engines drove a pair of Siemens-Schuckert 500 kVA generators which in turn drove a pair of Siemens 230 kW electric motors, each of which drove one of the tracks via the rear drive sprocket. The unorthodox design which resulted – with the turret positioned right at the front of the tank to allow room for all the drivetrain components – was designated the VK 45.01 (P). ▶

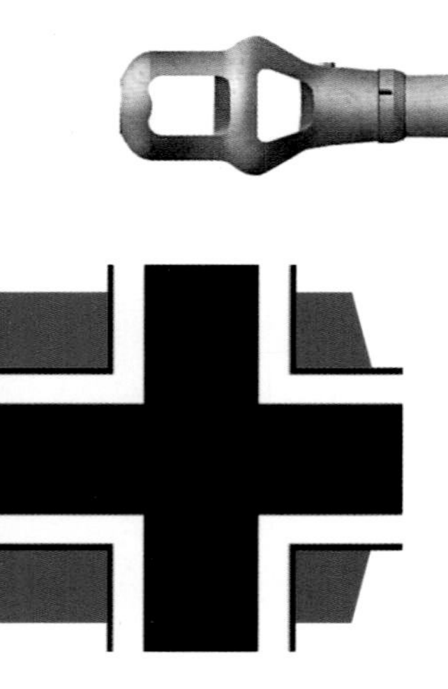

TIGER I AUSF. H ▶

Half a dozen Tigers of the 504th Heavy Panzer Battalion's 1st Company knocked out 40 tanks of the British 9th Armoured Division during the defence of Tunis on April 21, 1943, and forced the remainder to retreat. From their combat debut in December 1942 until their surrender to the British on May 12, 1943, the unit lost only six Tigers in action. Another three were captured, one broke down and burned and another nine were blown up by their crews. The remaining 15 Tigers were torched by their crews on May 12.

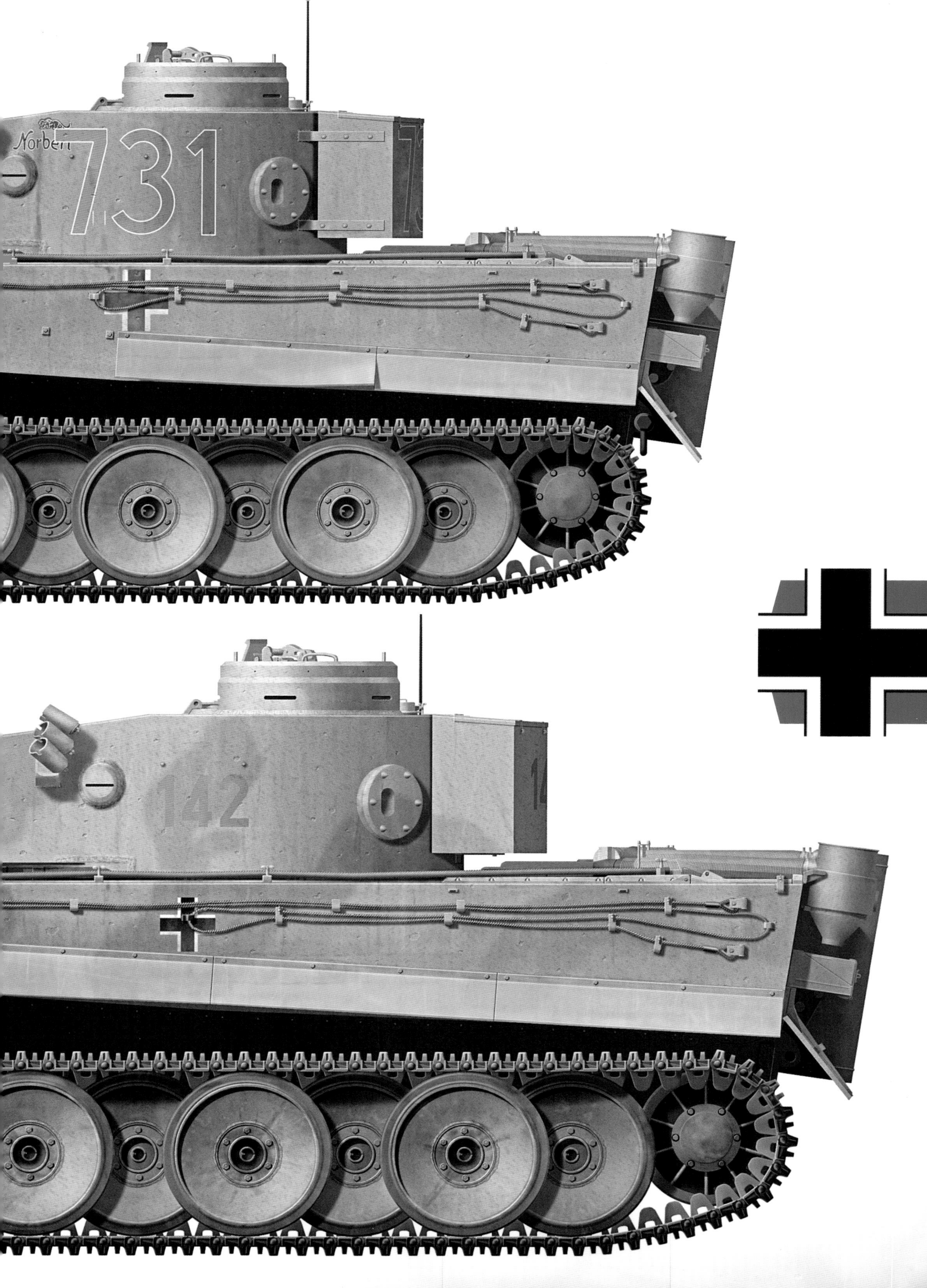
Norbert
731
142

On November 12, 1940, Waffen Prüfamt 6, the section of the Waffenamt responsible for combat vehicle design, contracted Nibelungenwerk in St Valentin, Austria, to built the prototypes of the VK 45.01 (P). After discussions lasting nearly three months, on April 25, 1941, Krupp's 88mm KwK L/56 gun was chosen for Porsche's new heavy tank. Krupp designed the turret too, with a wooden mock-up being completed on May 20, 1941.

Six days later, on May 26, 1941, a meeting was held with Hitler at which it was decided that both Henschel's VK 36.01 (H) and Porsche's VK 45.01 (P) would go into full production in parallel under what was known as the 'Tigerprogram' and that both would be armed with Rheinmetall-Borsig's 88mm Flak 41 gun. Both would have 100mm thick frontal armour and 60mm thick side armour and six examples of each would be ready for action by the summer of 1942. Crucially, both would also be fitted with deep wading gear. This meant that the bridge loading limit which had previously held down the weight of German tanks no longer applied – although the need to retain a width narrow enough for loading on to railway cars remained.

ON NOVEMBER 12, 1940, WAFFEN PRÜFAMT 6, THE SECTION OF THE WAFFENAMT RESPONSIBLE FOR COMBAT VEHICLE DESIGN, CONTRACTED NIBELUNGENWERK IN ST VALENTIN, AUSTRIA, TO BUILT THE PROTOTYPES OF THE VK 45.01 (P).

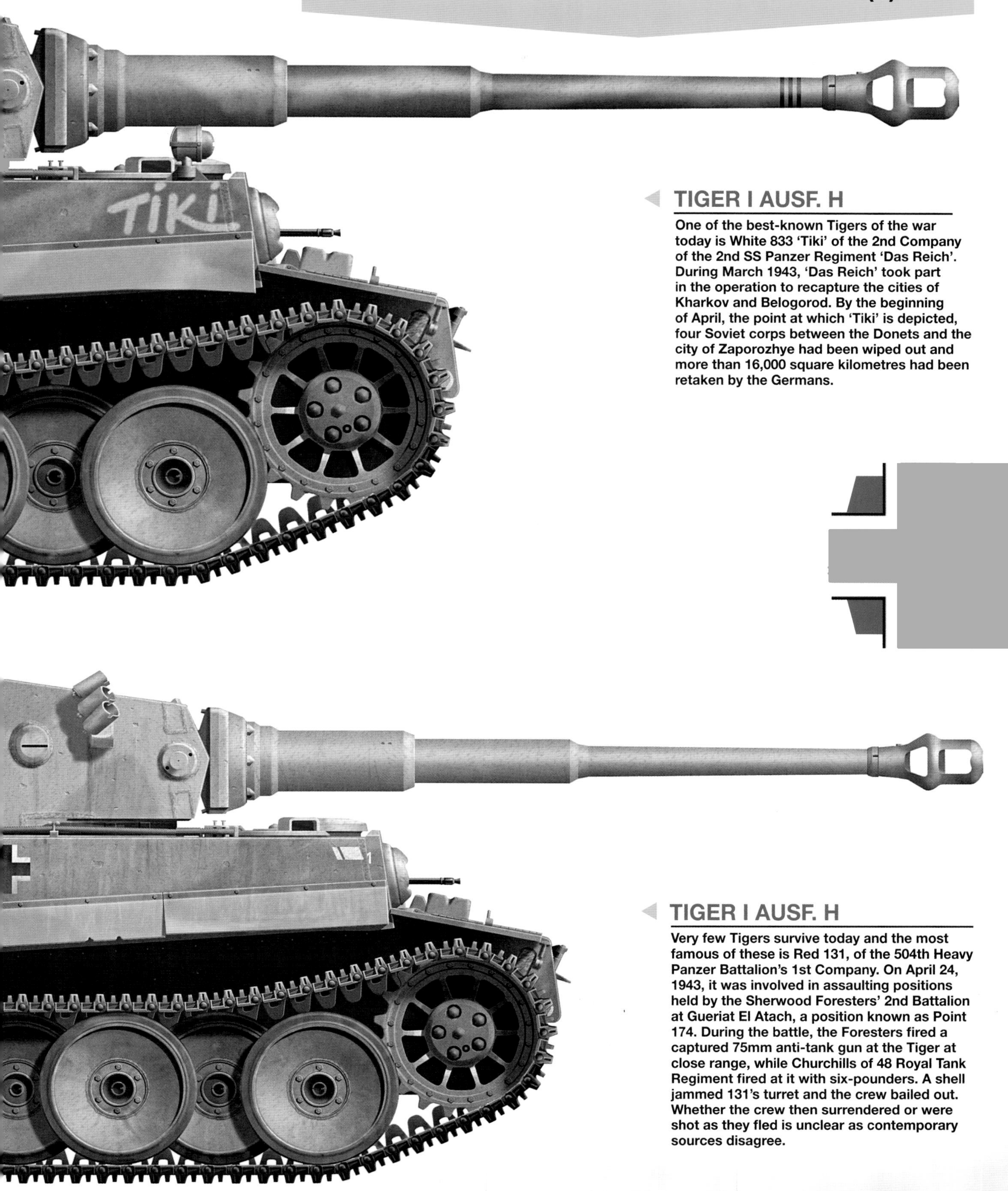

TIGER I AUSF. H

One of the best-known Tigers of the war today is White 833 'Tiki' of the 2nd Company of the 2nd SS Panzer Regiment 'Das Reich'. During March 1943, 'Das Reich' took part in the operation to recapture the cities of Kharkov and Belogorod. By the beginning of April, the point at which 'Tiki' is depicted, four Soviet corps between the Donets and the city of Zaporozhye had been wiped out and more than 16,000 square kilometres had been retaken by the Germans.

TIGER I AUSF. H

Very few Tigers survive today and the most famous of these is Red 131, of the 504th Heavy Panzer Battalion's 1st Company. On April 24, 1943, it was involved in assaulting positions held by the Sherwood Foresters' 2nd Battalion at Gueriat El Atach, a position known as Point 174. During the battle, the Foresters fired a captured 75mm anti-tank gun at the Tiger at close range, while Churchills of 48 Royal Tank Regiment fired at it with six-pounders. A shell jammed 131's turret and the crew bailed out. Whether the crew then surrendered or were shot as they fled is unclear as contemporary sources disagree.

TIGER I AUSF. E

This Tiger I, Green 1, was probably the vehicle of Major Gerhard Willing, the commander of the 506th Heavy Panzer Battalion's staff company. The tank is shown as it appeared at St Pölten, Austria, in August 1943 before it was loaded on to a train the following month and transported to the Zaporozhye-Dnieper Bend region of the USSR. From September 16 to September 27, the 506th was resupplied with 45 new Tiger Is.

After the meeting Waffen Prüfamt 6, commonly known by the abbreviated title Wa Prüf 6, came to understand that work on the Porsche design was already much further advanced than previously thought and contacted the company to see whether the already-designed Krupp turret could be modified to accept the Flak 41. Porsche responded on September 10, 1941, to state that the turret had been designed around the KwK L/56 and that there was no way in which it could be made to accept the Flak 41.

As a result, it was agreed that the first 100 production examples of the VK 45.01 (P) would have the original Krupp turret and that subsequent examples would be fitted with a newly designed turret capable of mounting the Flak 41. Krupp duly set to work on the turrets. The first eight had low sides and a flat, slightly sloped roof with a raised section in the middle to provide the gun with a greater degree of depression if necessary. The other 92 were slightly taller and horseshoe-shaped with a flat mantle at the front where the gun was fitted.

The armour protection of the VK 45.01 (P) exceeded the original specification, with 80mm on the sides rather than 60mm, but even so it was expected that the electro-mechanical drive would propel the vehicle along at a relatively brisk 35km/h. The suspension was by longitudinal torsion bar, allowing the overall height of the vehicle to be kept down. Weight, in the end, exceeded 59 tons.

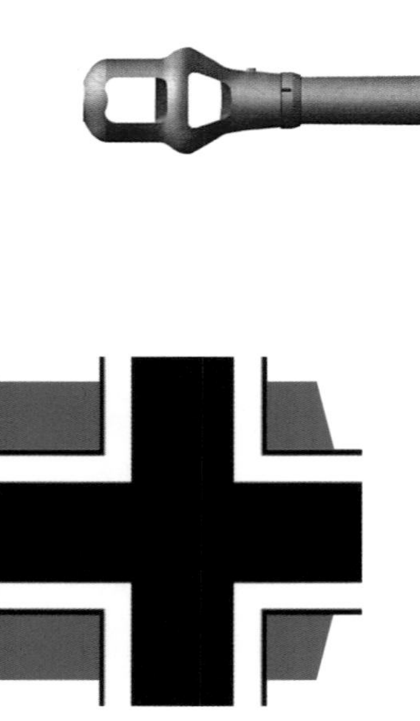

TIGER I AUSF. E

Yellow 324 of the 501st Heavy Panzer Battalion's 3rd Company, shown as it appeared in the area east of Minsk, USSR, during June 1944, has some interesting visual features: note the missing front outer road wheel; this was often removed to avoid clogging the drive train with mud and debris. Furthermore, the road wheels are all mottled with green and brown patches. This was contrary to regulations, as when rotating they increased visibility to the enemy and compromised the vehicle's concealment when on the move. The barrel is a replacement that is finished in a special dark grey heat-resistant lacquer paint.

TIGER I

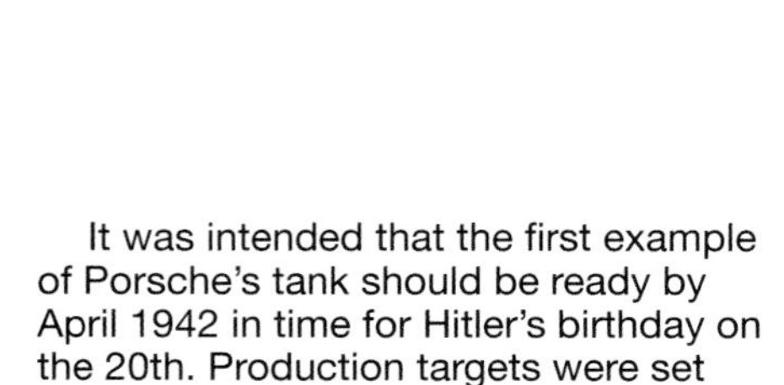

It was intended that the first example of Porsche's tank should be ready by April 1942 in time for Hitler's birthday on the 20th. Production targets were set on January 5, 1942, at 10 examples in May 1942, followed by another 10 in June, then 12 for July, 14 for August and 15 in September.

Meanwhile, Henschel had been confronted with a number of problems. Firstly, prior to the May 26 meeting, it had not even considered fitting an 88mm gun to the VK 36.01, let along the bulky Flak 41. Secondly, the VK 36.01 would need to become the VK 45.01 (H) due to the additional armour and larger engine it would require – but there was no time to develop a completely new drivetrain and running gear to compensate for the additional weight.

Initially, Henschel had hoped to use a modified version of the DW turret for the VK 36.01, carrying a 105mm gun, but this proposal was rejected at the May 26 meeting with Hitler. Another option was to fit a tapered bore 75mm gun known as Waffe 0725, but on September 27, 1941, Henschel had been informed by Oberst Sebastian Fichtner, the head of Wa Prüf 6, that Hitler had decided tapered bore weapons were not to be used for series production tanks.

Therefore, with too little time remaining to get a new turret designed, Henschel was forced to simply adopt the turret designed for the VK 45.01 (P) complete with its 88mm KwK L/56 gun. The VK 36.01 itself was fitted out with ▶

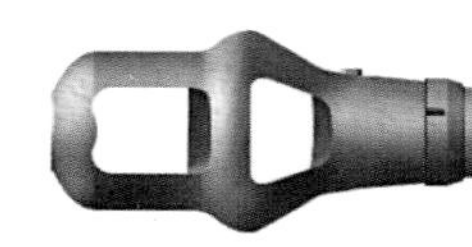

TIGER I AUSF. E ▶

Possibly commanded by Oberleutnant Dr Barkhausen, White 300 of the 505th Heavy Panzer Battalion's 3rd Company was knocked out by elements of the Soviet 307th division near the village of Ponyri, south of Orel in July of 1943. In two separate engagements on July 5 and July 15, the 505th destroyed 64 T-34s for the loss of one Tiger. However, even though the 505th only lost six Tigers in action overall during July, its operational strength fell from 31 tanks down to just three.

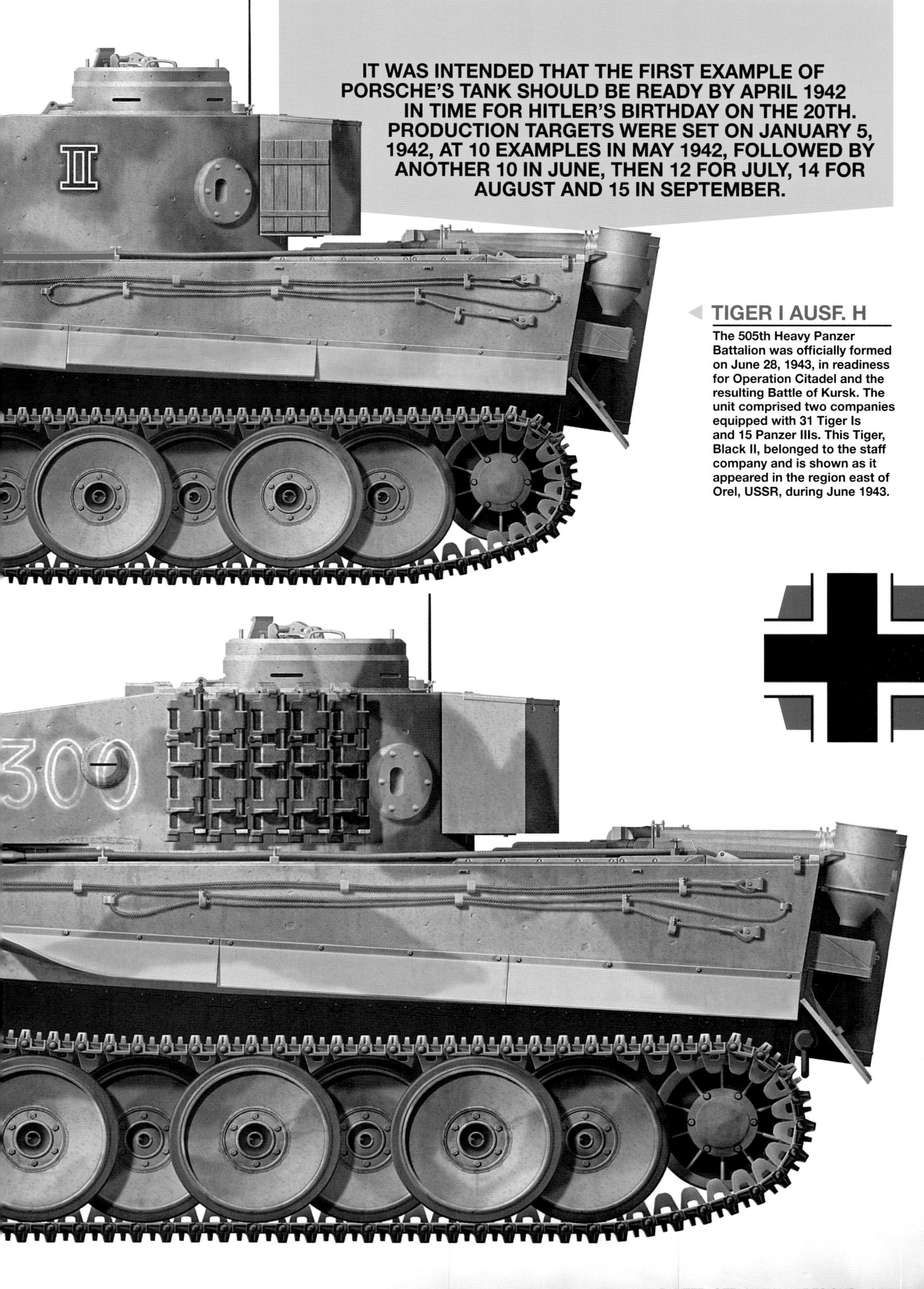

IT WAS INTENDED THAT THE FIRST EXAMPLE OF PORSCHE'S TANK SHOULD BE READY BY APRIL 1942 IN TIME FOR HITLER'S BIRTHDAY ON THE 20TH. PRODUCTION TARGETS WERE SET ON JANUARY 5, 1942, AT 10 EXAMPLES IN MAY 1942, FOLLOWED BY ANOTHER 10 IN JUNE, THEN 12 FOR JULY, 14 FOR AUGUST AND 15 IN SEPTEMBER.

TIGER I AUSF. H

The 505th Heavy Panzer Battalion was officially formed on June 28, 1943, in readiness for Operation Citadel and the resulting Battle of Kursk. The unit comprised two companies equipped with 31 Tiger Is and 15 Panzer IIIs. This Tiger, Black II, belonged to the staff company and is shown as it appeared in the region east of Orel, USSR, during June 1943.

TIGER I

TIGER I AUSF. E

Black 213, shown here in the Tjernovo-Leningrad area of the USSR during July 1943, was commanded by the tank ace Oberleutnant Otto Carius of the 502nd Heavy Panzer Battalion's 2nd Company, who is credited with destroying more than 150 enemy tanks. Otto's small and slim stature resulted in him being sent home twice as "not fit for service, at present underweight". He was permanently drafted in May of 1940 however, and was eventually awarded the Oak Leaves to the Knights Cross in recognition of his accomplishments in combat as well as his military leadership.

a new engine, the 650hp 12-cylinder Maybach HL 210 P45, new fuel tanks, a new cooling system and new equipment that would enable it to ford rivers and streams. However, in order to speed up the development process, as many existing components as possible were used, in particular the DW's running gear, torsion bar suspension, Henschel L 600 C steering and Maybach Olvar 40 12 16 transmission. Krupp's Porsche turret was switched from an electric traverse to hydraulic and received a new travel lock.

The VK 36.01's boxy hull was extended rather than being reshaped. It was widened at the sides to create 'panniers' over the vehicle's tracks which could house its radiators and the engine compartment was expanded with a new hatch being fitted on top. Armour at the front was 100mm thick, including 100mm on the turret front, and 80mm on the superstructure side plates. It was only 60mm on the completely flat vertical hull side plates, however. The VK 45.01 (H) was fitted with a retractable 'Vorpanzer' shield at the front to provide extra protection for the tracks and

TIGER I AUSF. H

This is the Tiger of SS-Hauptsturmführer Zimmermann, commander of the 8th Company of the 2nd SS Panzer Regiment 'Das Reich'. White S01 is depicted in the USSR on July 5, 1943. A week later Zimmermann was wounded at Kursk and his temporary replacements, SS-Hauptsturmführer Lorenz and SS-Obersturmführer Theiss were both killed in action within four days. The latter was standing within the commander's cupola of his Tiger when it was hit by an anti-tank gun and blown clean off, taking his head with it. This was apparently a common problem with the early type drum cupola. Note the devil insignia painted in white on the turret: this badge was of Russian origin and evidently used by the locals to fend off evil spirits.

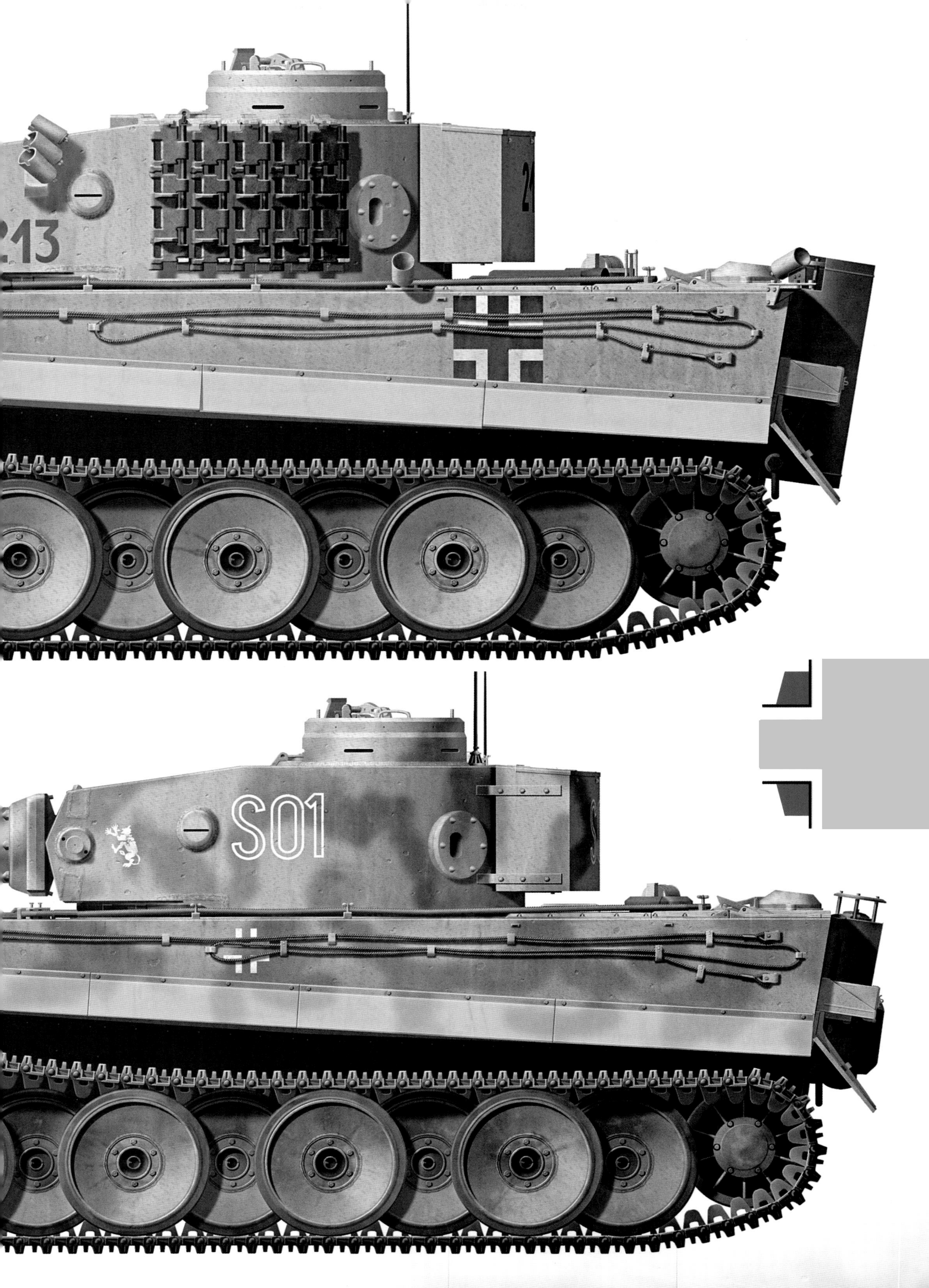
213
S01

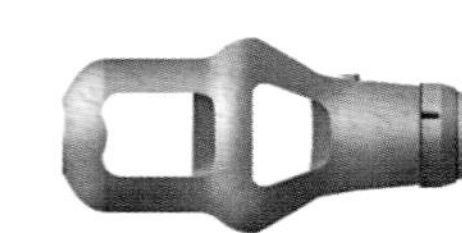

TIGER I

TIGER I AUSF. E

With the addition of armoured personnel carriers and Tigers in May 1943, Infantry Division 'Grossdeutschland' was re-designated Panzer Grenadier Division 'Grossdeutschland'. One of those Tigers was Black B22, shown here in August 1943. The newly re-equipped division was subordinated to the XLVIII Panzer Corps, and played a major role alongside the II SS Panzer Corps in Operation Citadel. During the first week, the division's Tiger company advanced over 30km and destroyed nearly 60 Russian tanks for the loss of six Tigers.

drive sprockets – a feature that was not carried on into series production.

Sixty-four rounds for the main gun were stored inside the panniers, lying horizontally in covered bins, while another 16 rounds were kept in bins on the hull sides. Another six sat in a bin beside the driver and yet another six lay in a bin under the floor beneath the turret in the centre of the tank. For close protection, the vehicle had a hull-mounted MG 34 and another mounted in the turret, with a total of 4800 rounds between them. On the front of the tank was a pair of headlights, one at each corner.

On March 2, 1942, both the Porsche and Henschel designs were given the designation 'Tiger' but the first Henschel prototype did not even receive its lightly modified turret from Krupp until April 11, 1942. ▶

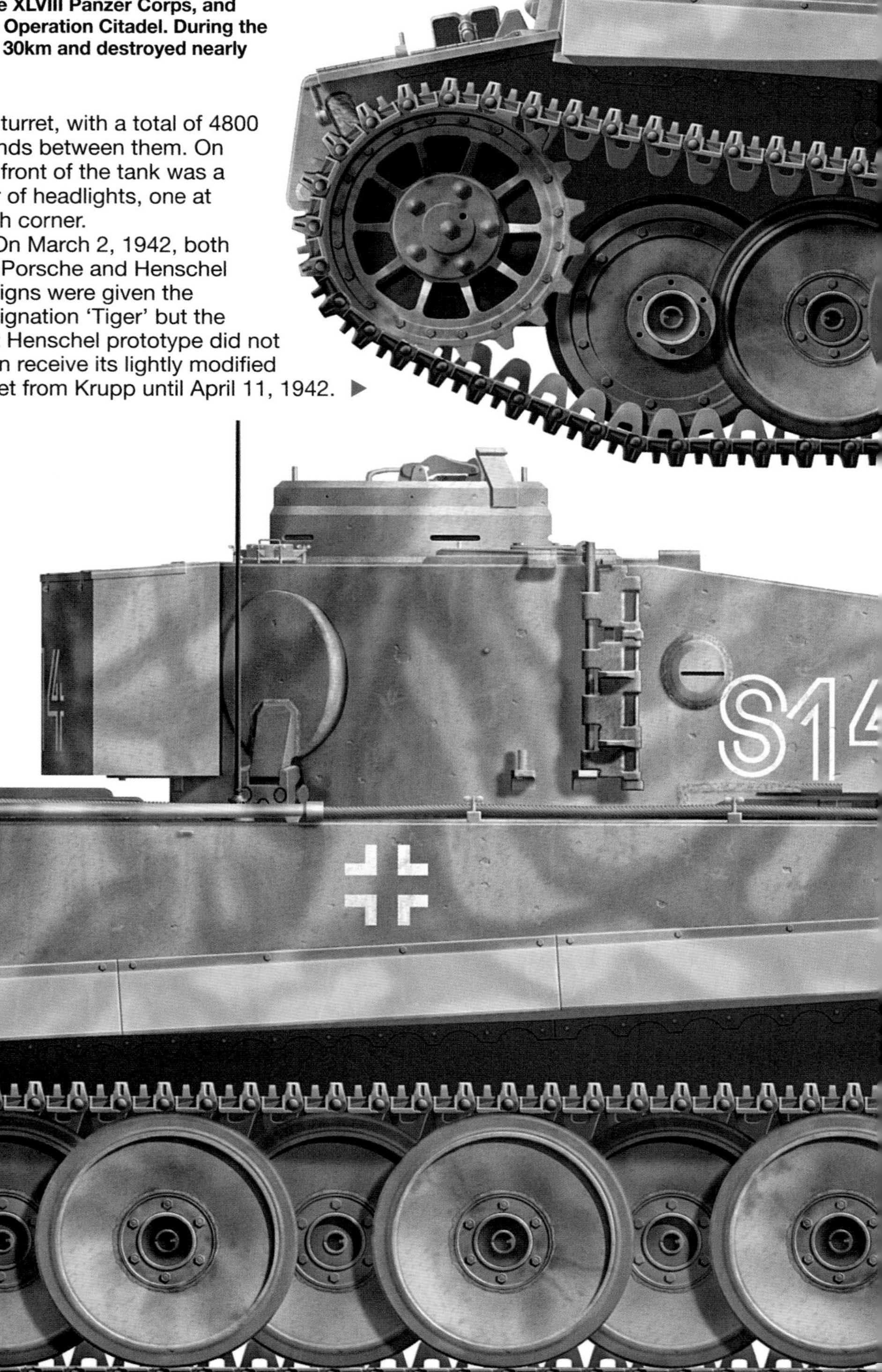

TIGER I AUSF. E

White S14 was commanded by SS-Oberscharführer Kamarad and was one of several newly manufactured Tigers that the 1st SS Panzer Regiment 'Leibstandarte SS Adolf Hitler' received while being rested and refitted in Reggio, Italy, during August 1943. Later that month new personnel arrived from the Senne training camp to organise the new 101st SS Heavy Panzer Battalion. On September 16, awards were handed out to those who had participated in Operation Citadel. During this battle the unit had destroyed 150 tanks, 71 anti-tank guns and six artillery pieces, losing only one Tiger in the process.

TIGER I

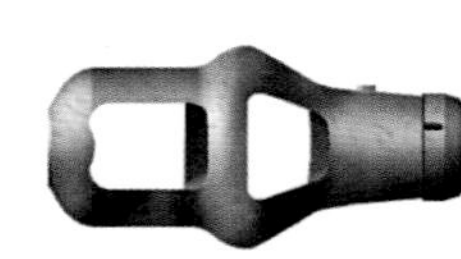

TIGER I AUSF. E

Thirteen Tigers of the 506th Heavy Panzer Battalion's 2nd Company, including Red 6, attacked Soviet forces north of Blisnezy on September 21, 1943. The 506th lost eight tanks in the Zaporozhye area during the month.

The Henschel and Porsche Tigers were duly inspected by Hitler on his birthday as planned and both were ordered into production in parallel.

Both types were beset by mechanical problems – the Porsche Tiger because of its complicated drivetrain and the Henschel Tiger because it had been put together so quickly from parts intended for smaller, lighter tanks. The latter also suffered from leaky gaskets and seals. Just nine Henschel Tigers had been delivered by August 1942 but the Porsche Tiger was still undeliverable. In September, Hitler ordered that only the Henschel Tiger should continue into ongoing production with the Posche Tiger chassis, when they were completed, being used as the basis of a new heavy assault gun – what would become the Ferdinand, later known as the Elefant.

The first full production Tiger I was completed on May 17, 1942, and sent for testing at the German Army's Kummersdorf proving grounds. Rather than the Vorpanzer shield, it had track mudguards made from sheet metal fitted at the front of the vehicle but no mudguards on the sides. Beginning in August 1942, a set of three smoke ▶

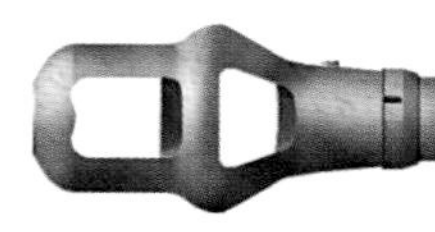

TIGER I AUSF. E

Black 300 was the vehicle of Knight's Cross holder Oberleutnant Walter Scherf, the commander of the 503rd Heavy Panzer Battalion's 3rd Company, during September 1943. At this time German forces were retreating across the Eastern Front and immobilised tanks were often left behind. Despite this fact, many vehicles were eventually retrieved and on September 13 Oberleutnant Scherf, together with two other operational Tigers, managed to tow eight of their damaged tanks to Paraskoweja. Unteroffizier Rubble's Tiger 114 was saved by loading it on to a railway car that was pushed by 30 soldiers across a railway bridge over the river Dnieper. On September 22, the combat diary of the 503rd concluded that since July 5 the unit had destroyed 501 tanks, 388 antitank guns, 97 artillery pieces and eight aircraft, losing just 16 of its Tigers.

6
300

TIGER I

TIGER I AUSF. E

The camouflage painted on to Black 332 of the 503rd Heavy Panzer Battalion's 3rd Company is unusual. The overall colour is definitely darker than RAL 7028 Dunkelgelb but too light for RAL 7021 Panzergrau. It is believed that this tank was originally destined for North Africa, but instead ended up with the 503rd on the Eastern Front. Therefore, this Tiger was probably camouflaged in RAL 8000 Grünbraun. This is how it appeared at Znamenka in the USSR during October 1943.

grenade launchers was mounted on either side of the turret.

The following month, all-round mudguards were added. Each was made up of four sections which were bolted to the sides of the tank's hull. In addition, a metal box was added to the left rear hull so that track adjustment and replacement tools could be kept together in one easily accessible location.

While early Tigers had been fitted with cross-country tracks on the left and right sides which mirrored one another, in October this was changed to all Tiger cross-country tracks being identical and interchangeable – the tracks on the right were simply mounted in reverse to the tracks on the left. This evidently resulted in Tigers pulling slightly to one side while travelling forwards. The following month, Henschel began fitting new air filters to Tigers that were intended for service in hot dusty locations such as Africa, Italy and the southern parts of Russia. In addition, new hinged track mudguards were installed at the front and rear of the vehicle.

From December 1942, the Tiger's turret was modified to include an ▶

TIGER I AUSF. E

The 3rd Company of the 504th Heavy Panzer Battalion was a Funklenk unit equipped with the NSU Springer remote control mine demolition vehicle. Each Tiger, including White 331, all had an antenna mounted on the right side of the turret front. On June 22, 1944, four Tigers from the 504th engaged a formation of 25 Sherman tanks in the area around Massa Marittima, north-western Italy. Eleven Shermans were knocked-out and set on fire. The remaining 14 crews open their hatches and fled, leaving the tanks to the Germans. No Tigers were lost.

332
31

TIGER I

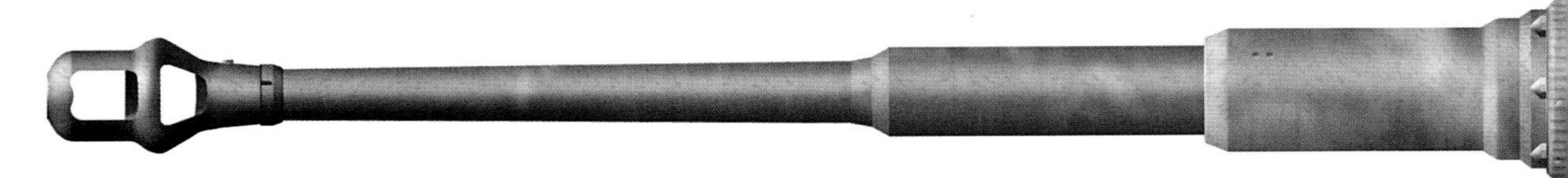

TIGER I AUSF. E

White C was a command vehicle of the 507th Heavy Panzer Battalion's staff company and is depicted as it appeared at Lemberg in the Ternopil region of the Ukraine during the summer of 1944. The 507th lost 11 Tigers in July 1944, two of them destroyed by their crews.

escape hatch on its rear right wall, the commander's seat was made adjustable and a large bin was mounted on the back of the turret to increase the tank's general stowage capacity – this latter being fitted to all 70 Tigers having been built by the end of 1942.

A heat guard and deflector were added in January 1943 to shroud the tank's exhaust mufflers and prevent flames from giving the vehicle's position away, and in March a metal shield was fitted to protect the tank commander from back-blast when the main gun was fired. A periscope for the loader was also added to the roof of the turret.

Perhaps the greatest change made to the Tiger during its entire production run occurred in May 1943 when the new 690hp Maybach HL 230 P45 replaced the HL 210 P45, which had powered the first 250 examples. The HL 210 had a displacement of 21.353 litres or 1303 cu in, a bore of 125mm and a stroke of 145mm. On the HL 230, displacement was 23.095 litres or 1409.3 cu in, bore was increased by 5mm up to 130mm and stroke remained the same. The new engine had two air filters and required changes to the cooling system. In practice, the additional 40hp made little difference to the Tiger's performance however.

It had a maximum speed of 45.4km/h but its top road speed was 20km/h, dropping to 15km/h cross-country. Its range was 195km when travelling by road and 110km cross-country.

The following month the turret-mounted smoke launchers were deleted from the design due to the danger of

TIGER I AUSF. E

Tigers of the 507th Heavy Panzer Battalion can be identified by the extra track links mounted on their turrets. This is White 100 of the 1st Company, pictured in the Ternopil area of the Ukraine during the summer of 1944. It may have been the vehicle of company commander Hauptmann Siegfried Holzheid.

TIGER I

their being accidentally ignited by small arms fire from the enemy. The turret underwent a redesign in July 1943, with the hinged hatch of the commander's cupola being replaced with a new swivelling one. Armoured shields were fitted to protect the periscopes and the roof-mounted exhaust fan was repositioned to provide improved ventilation for the crew compartment.

Inside the turret, the awkward metal shield installed to protect the commander from breech blow-back was replaced with a far more convenient strip of fireproof cloth and a new turret lock was introduced. Externally, Tigers built during and after July had their two headlights replaced with a single one fitted to the top left of the forward superstructure.

All the seals, pipes and other equipment necessary for the tank to drive through water above its roofline were removed from the design in August, significantly simplifying the production of numerous assemblies. Even without this gear, thanks to some simple gaskets the tank was still capable of crossing rivers up to a depth of 1.5m.

Zimmerit anti-magnetic mine paste was applied from September and two months later a fan, ducting and vents were installed in the firewall at the front of the vehicle to extract fumes coming from the gearbox and brakes.

An external travel lock for the main gun was also installed on the rear of the tank which, used in conjunction with the internal travel lock, helped to prevent the delicate gun sight from being shifted out of alignment when travelling over rough ground. This meant that the turret had to be positioned with the gun ▶

TIGER I AUSF. E ▶

This tank was the first Tiger the 102nd SS Heavy Panzer Battalion lost in Normandy, probably on July 10, 1944. White 221 was later found knocked-out, and the entire crew, including the commander Willy Endmann, were missing and presumed KIA.

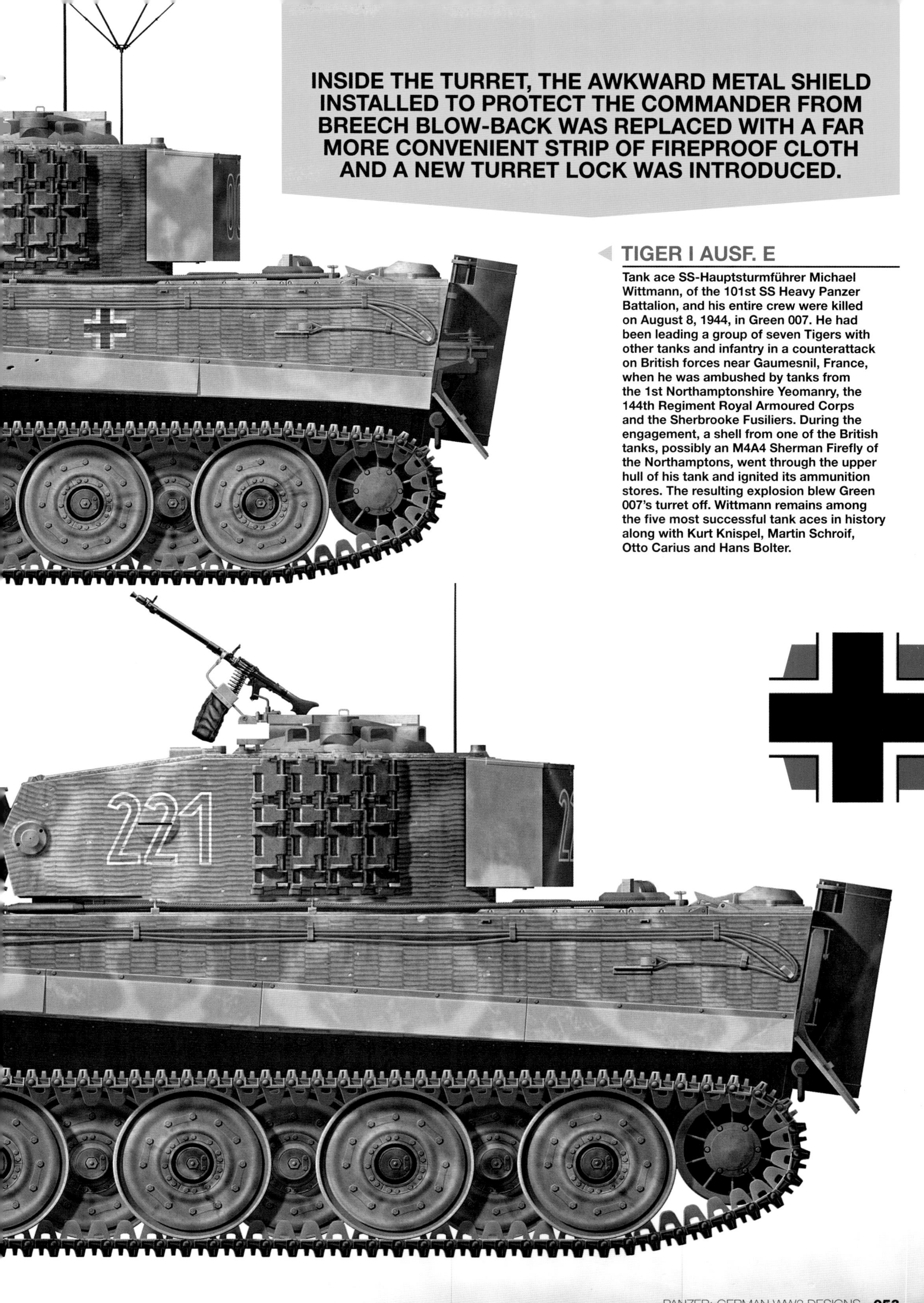

INSIDE THE TURRET, THE AWKWARD METAL SHIELD INSTALLED TO PROTECT THE COMMANDER FROM BREECH BLOW-BACK WAS REPLACED WITH A FAR MORE CONVENIENT STRIP OF FIREPROOF CLOTH AND A NEW TURRET LOCK WAS INTRODUCED.

TIGER I AUSF. E

Tank ace SS-Hauptsturmführer Michael Wittmann, of the 101st SS Heavy Panzer Battalion, and his entire crew were killed on August 8, 1944, in Green 007. He had been leading a group of seven Tigers with other tanks and infantry in a counterattack on British forces near Gaumesnil, France, when he was ambushed by tanks from the 1st Northamptonshire Yeomanry, the 144th Regiment Royal Armoured Corps and the Sherbrooke Fusiliers. During the engagement, a shell from one of the British tanks, possibly an M4A4 Sherman Firefly of the Northamptons, went through the upper hull of his tank and ignited its ammunition stores. The resulting explosion blew Green 007's turret off. Wittmann remains among the five most successful tank aces in history along with Kurt Knispel, Martin Schroif, Otto Carius and Hans Bolter.

TIGER I

fixed facing the rear while the tank was moving forwards and also meant that a crewman had to get out of the tank to free the gun before it could engage in combat. Meanwhile, the external track replacement tool box was deleted.

In December 1943, half a dozen raised sections in the shape of chevrons were added to the face of every track link to help improve traction when travelling over snow and ice. Additionally, the now single headlight was repositioned to the centre of the vehicle's forward plate.

A lingering hangover from the deep fording kit, a suction pump and discharge pipe, were deleted from January 1944 – as was the turret pistol port. In place of the latter, a roof-mounted close defence weapon was due to be fitted, although this did not actually appear until March 1944. In the meantime, in February, road wheels with steel tyres from the Tiger II, which had internal rubber cushioning and were designed to cope with extremely heavy vehicles, were added to the Tiger I production line. As a result, the number of road wheels per axle could be reduced from three down to two.

An engine coolant heater, incorporating a blowtorch, was also installed to the left of the engine bay so that coolant could be warmed before the crew attempted to start the engine during extremely cold weather. In March, in addition to Tigers receiving a close defence weapon which could fire smoke rounds, signal rounds or grenades, they were also fitted with a thicker 40mm

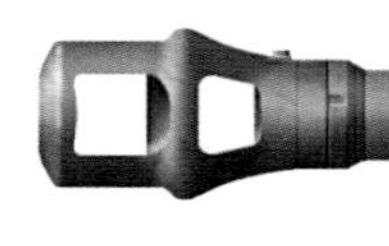

TIGER I AUSF. E

This vehicle was commanded by SS-Obersturmführer Helmut 'Bubi' Wendorff of the 101st SS Heavy Panzer Battalion on August 14, 1944, when he and two of his crew were killed when engaging Sherman tanks at less than 30 metres. The battle took place at Potigny, Normandy, France. Wendorff's gunner SS-Rottenführer Walter Lau hit the first Sherman but Yellow 211 was quickly hit by the second Sherman. Only Lau and newly promoted driver SS-Unterscharführer Franz Elmer escaped with their lives.

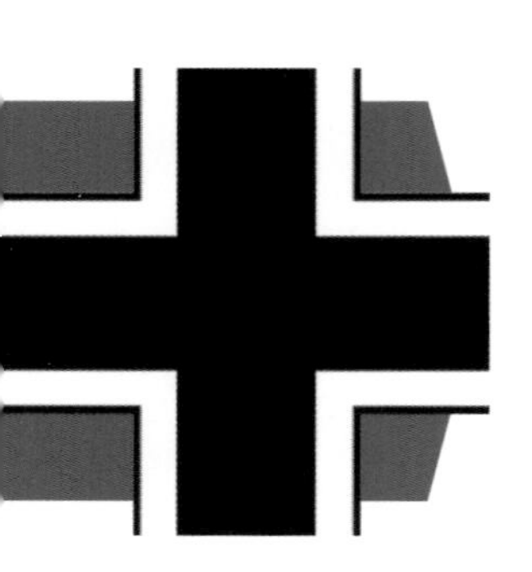

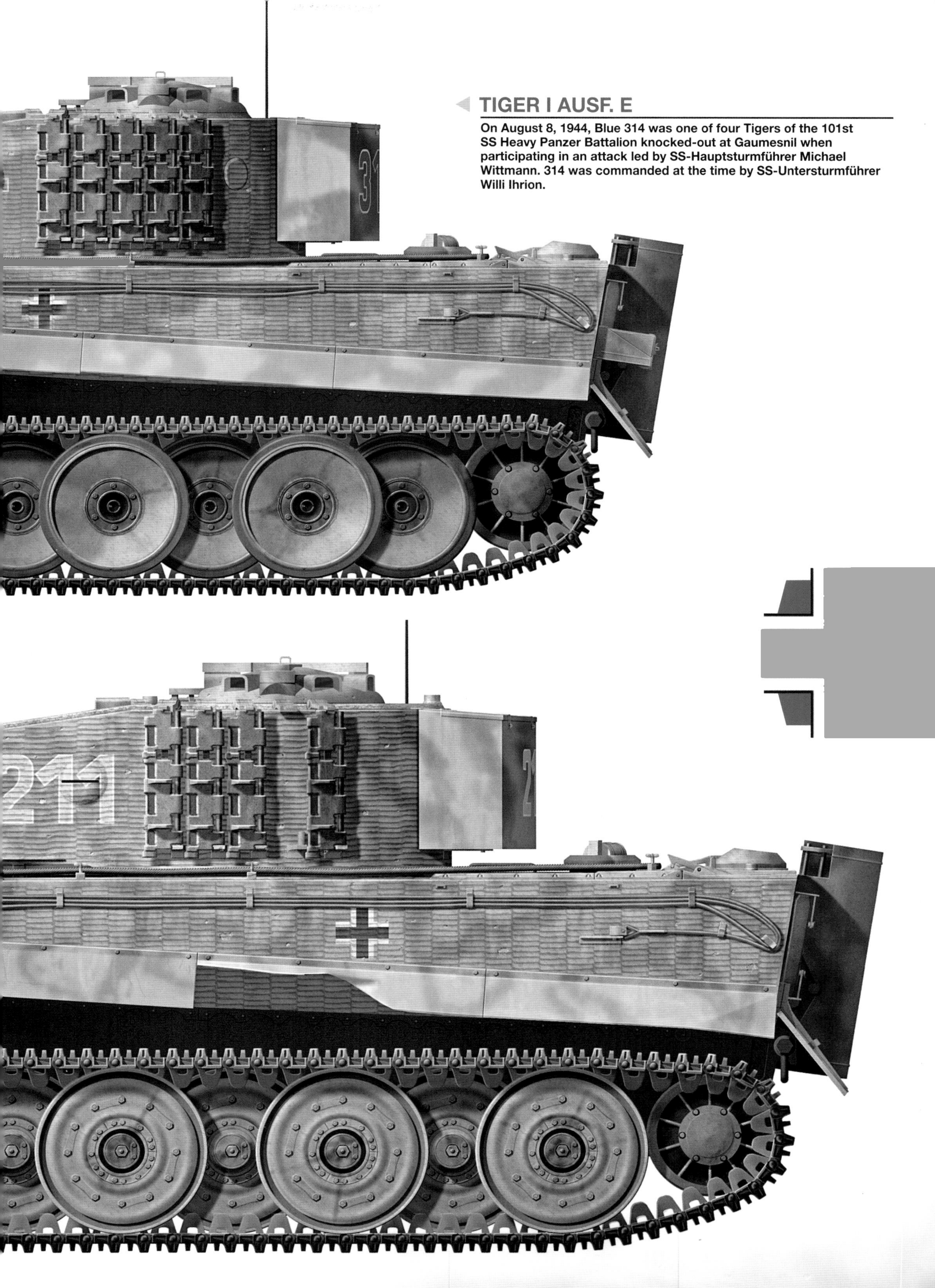

TIGER I AUSF. E

On August 8, 1944, Blue 314 was one of four Tigers of the 101st SS Heavy Panzer Battalion knocked-out at Gaumesnil when participating in an attack led by SS-Hauptsturmführer Michael Wittmann. 314 was commanded at the time by SS-Untersturmführer Willi Ihrion.

TIGER I

TIGER I AUSF. E

White 132 was commanded by SS-Oberscharführer Walther Knecht of the 102nd SS Heavy Panzer Battalion's 1st Company. Knecht's driver, only known as 'Heini', managed to drive it all the way from Normandy back to the Cologne area, a distance of 650km, in early September of 1944. He was awarded the Iron Cross first class for that accomplishment.

armoured turret roof. Previously, armour protection at this point was only 25mm.

From April 1944, the vehicle's upper fuel tanks were fitted with a wooden covering to prevent shell fragments and bullets from landing on them after passing through the air vents on the rear engine deck. The tank was also fitted with a new gun sight at this time which allowed the gunner to choose between two magnification settings – 2.5x and 5x.

From June, sockets were welded on to the turret roof so that a jib boom could be fitted for lifting out the vehicle's engine.

Production of the Tiger I ceased in August 1944 with a final six examples rolling off the factory line. Still, a final minor developmental change was approved in October 1944 when crews were given permission to carry 16 additional rounds of ammunition for the main gun along the internal sides of the hull, strapped in place above the ammunition bins.

Despite production having ended eight months earlier, some Tigers continued to fight until the end of the war. And even by May 1945, the Tiger's heavy frontal armour and fearsome gun made it a force to be reckoned with on the battlefield. ●

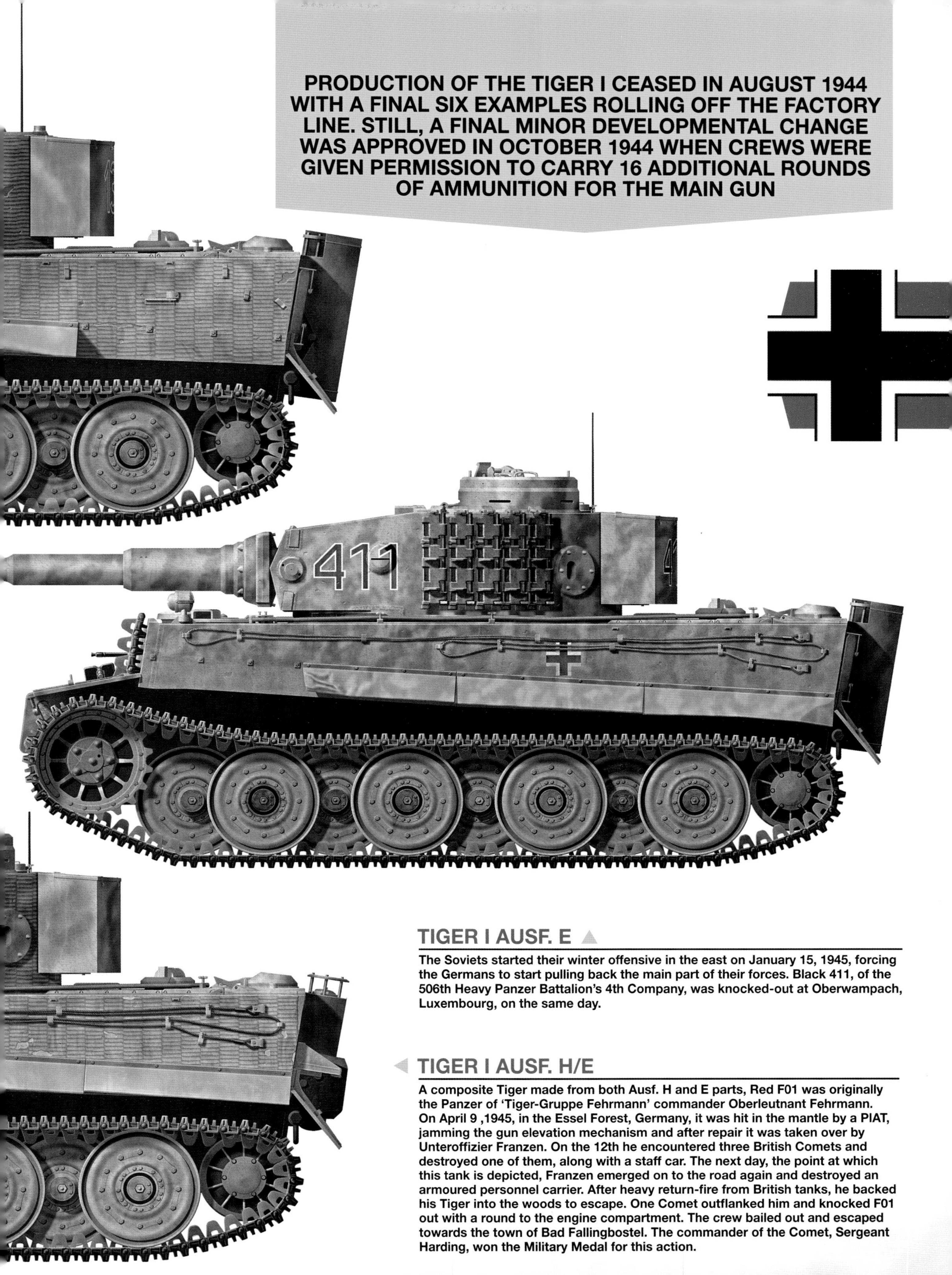

PRODUCTION OF THE TIGER I CEASED IN AUGUST 1944 WITH A FINAL SIX EXAMPLES ROLLING OFF THE FACTORY LINE. STILL, A FINAL MINOR DEVELOPMENTAL CHANGE WAS APPROVED IN OCTOBER 1944 WHEN CREWS WERE GIVEN PERMISSION TO CARRY 16 ADDITIONAL ROUNDS OF AMMUNITION FOR THE MAIN GUN

TIGER I AUSF. E ▲

The Soviets started their winter offensive in the east on January 15, 1945, forcing the Germans to start pulling back the main part of their forces. Black 411, of the 506th Heavy Panzer Battalion's 4th Company, was knocked-out at Oberwampach, Luxembourg, on the same day.

◄ TIGER I AUSF. H/E

A composite Tiger made from both Ausf. H and E parts, Red F01 was originally the Panzer of 'Tiger-Gruppe Fehrmann' commander Oberleutnant Fehrmann. On April 9 ,1945, in the Essel Forest, Germany, it was hit in the mantle by a PIAT, jamming the gun elevation mechanism and after repair it was taken over by Unteroffizier Franzen. On the 12th he encountered three British Comets and destroyed one of them, along with a staff car. The next day, the point at which this tank is depicted, Franzen emerged on to the road again and destroyed an armoured personnel carrier. After heavy return-fire from British tanks, he backed his Tiger into the woods to escape. One Comet outflanked him and knocked F01 out with a round to the engine compartment. The crew bailed out and escaped towards the town of Bad Fallingbostel. The commander of the Comet, Sergeant Harding, won the Military Medal for this action.

1943-1945

PANTHER

Combining a highly effective gun and sloped hull armour with excellent mobility, the Panther is regarded by many as the best tank of the Second World War. It had its flaws but, in good repair and with a skilled crew, it was a world-beater.

The German armoured divisions participating in the invasion of the Soviet Union on June 22, 1941, had around 3000 tanks between them, including 700 Panzer IIIs, 440 Panzer IVs and 200 StuGs. The opponents they encountered initially were equipped with poorly armed and armoured BT-series and T-26 tanks. These were destroyed in their hundreds as Germany's forces advanced rapidly through the Ukraine, the Baltic states, Belorussia and northwest Russia.

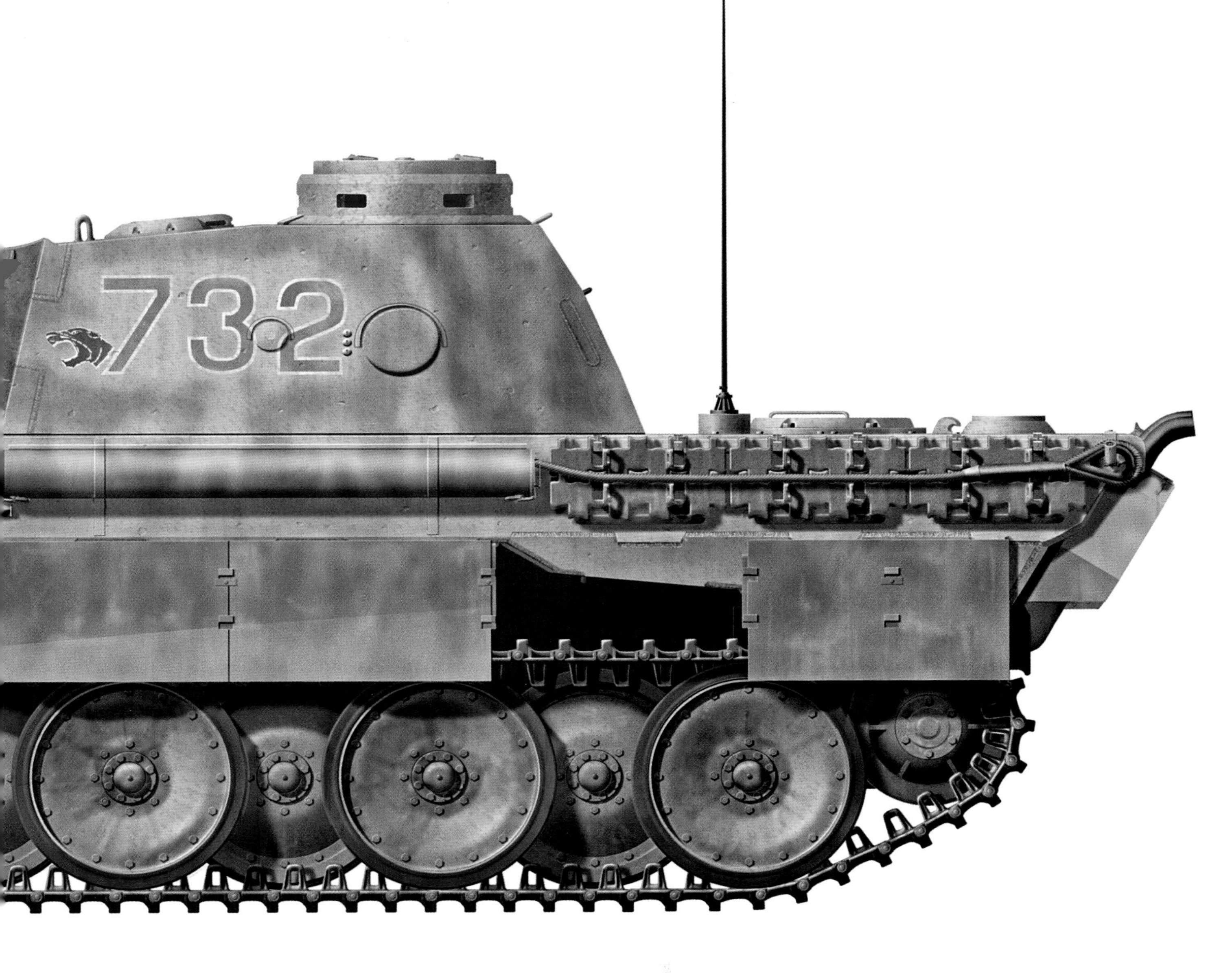

PANTHER AUSF. D ▲

This is Black 732 of the 52nd Panzer Battalion's 7th Company as it appeared at Kursk during July 1943. On July 8, during the Battle of Kursk, the Germans intercepted a radio message in which the Soviets reported their first sighting of the Panther. It read: "Enemy has introduced new tank, shape roughly similar to 'Tridsatchedverka' (T-34). The tank is heavily armoured, the weight is estimated at 40-50 tons. Armament is probably 88mm AA gun. We had losses at combat ranges beyond 2000 metres."

But German forces quickly ran into a new and unexpected enemy – the T-34 medium tank. While its forward and side armour was only adequately thick for the time at 45mm and 40mm respectively, the fact that this armour was sloped significantly increased its true horizontal thickness and dramatically increased the likelihood that incoming shells would simply ricochet off it.

To their surprise and horror, German tank crews found that penetrating the T-34's armour was very difficult. Had it not been for the scarcity of early T-34s and their crews' poor training and lack of radio equipment the German invasion might have quickly ground to a halt. As it was, the German army's commanders were left shaken by their forces' encounters with this remarkable machine.

Engineers from the German tank manufacturers and Waffenamt staff were sent to the Eastern Front to spend three days studying captured T-34s from November 18 to November 21, 1941. During their visit, Generaloberst Heinz Guderian suggested that the fastest way to counter the T-34 would be simply to copy it, but this idea was quickly rejected because the technology used to create the Soviet tank was incompatible with German production lines. For example, all German tanks had petrol engines, whereas the T-34 ran on diesel and incorporating a petrol engine would have entailed a significant redesign.

Instead it was decided that the next generation of German tanks should incorporate the T-34's best features, particularly its sloped armour but also the idea of having a long gun barrel overhanging the front of the tank – which ▶

PANTHER

the Germans had previously thought impractical.

According to CIOS report XXIX-22 History of German Tank Development by Robert Schilling, dated June 25, 1945: "During 1940 and 1941 various tanks of the 30 to 35-ton class were under development and tentatively scheduled for 1942 production. All these plans were dropped in the first months after the invasion of Russia when the T-34 tank was encountered.

"This tank must have made a deep impression on all men concerned with the German tank industry because almost every engineer interrogated admitted that many of its features were copied in Germany. The two most important features seem to have been the gun with large overhang, which Germans had thought impractical, and the ballistically favourable shape of the hull.

"In order to be sure to overmatch the T-34, and any developments of it that the Russians might have, the German staff decided to go immediately up to tanks of 45 to 50-ton size, and to guns of 88mm. This meant that for the first time a new model had to be planned without being able to use components already on test.

"Besides that, the development time had to be shortened to a little over one ▶

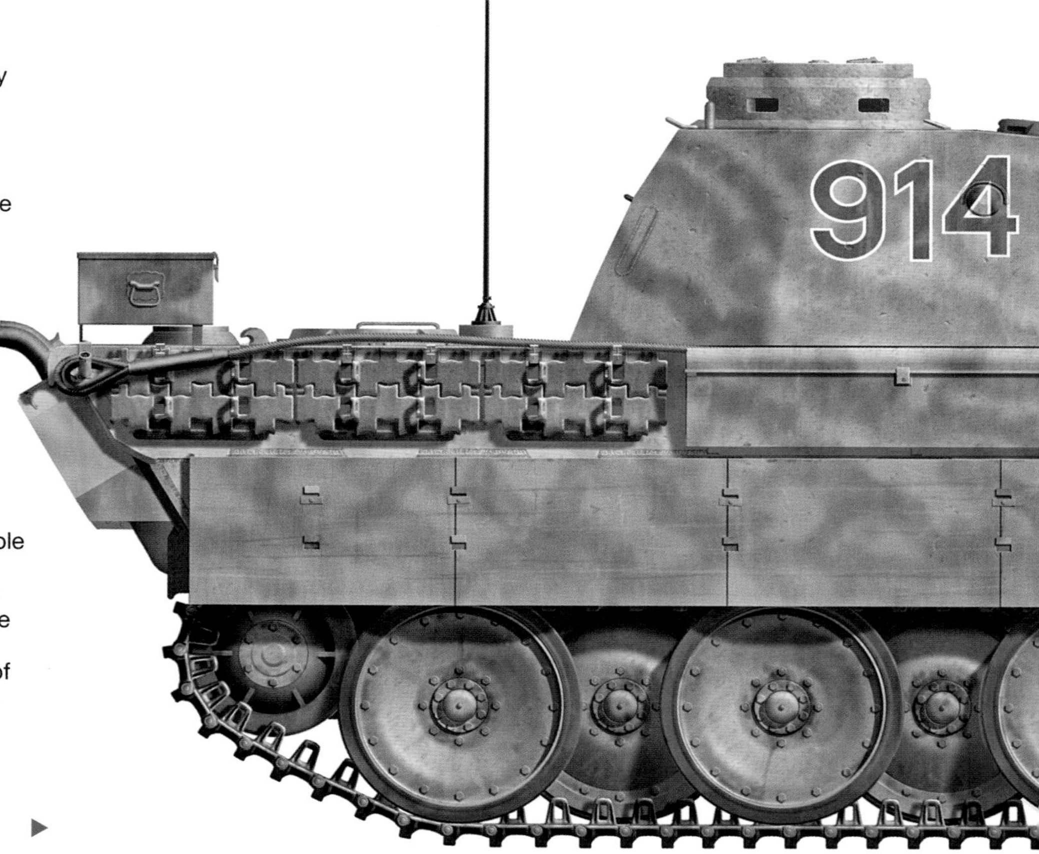

THE TWO MOST IMPORTANT FEATURES SEEM TO HAVE BEEN THE GUN WITH LARGE OVERHANG, WHICH GERMANS HAD THOUGHT IMPRACTICAL, AND THE BALLISTICALLY FAVOURABLE SHAPE OF THE HULL

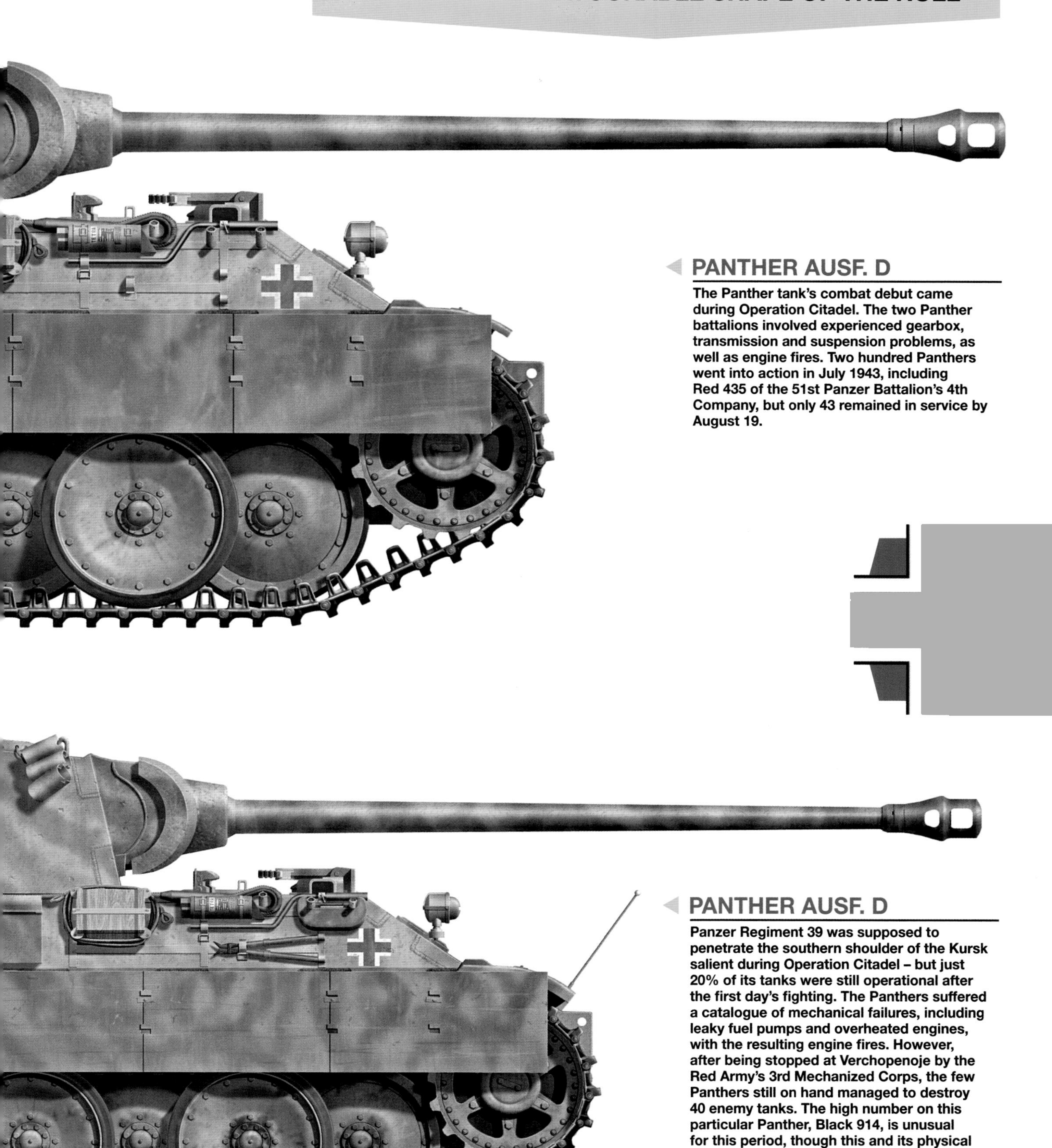

PANTHER AUSF. D

The Panther tank's combat debut came during Operation Citadel. The two Panther battalions involved experienced gearbox, transmission and suspension problems, as well as engine fires. Two hundred Panthers went into action in July 1943, including Red 435 of the 51st Panzer Battalion's 4th Company, but only 43 remained in service by August 19.

PANTHER AUSF. D

Panzer Regiment 39 was supposed to penetrate the southern shoulder of the Kursk salient during Operation Citadel – but just 20% of its tanks were still operational after the first day's fighting. The Panthers suffered a catalogue of mechanical failures, including leaky fuel pumps and overheated engines, with the resulting engine fires. However, after being stopped at Verchopenoje by the Red Army's 3rd Mechanized Corps, the few Panthers still on hand managed to destroy 40 enemy tanks. The high number on this particular Panther, Black 914, is unusual for this period, though this and its physical features suggest that it was one of five tanks associated with the staff company of the 52nd Panzer Battalion's reconnaissance unit. This is how it appeared near Belgorod, Russia, on July 4, 1943.

PANTHER

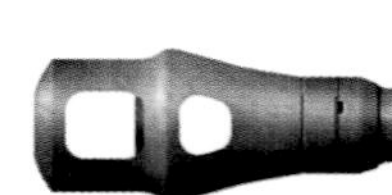

PANTHER AUSF. D

A general retreat from the Kursk salient was ordered on July 20, 1943, by which point the Panther units committed had lost 56 vehicles. A further 85 Panthers were non-functional but could at least be repaired by Panzer Regiment 39's own maintenance units. Sixteen were so seriously damaged that they had to be sent back to Germany. Among the survivors was Black 833 of the 52nd Panzer Battalion's 8th Company. The victory claims submitted by the Panther units during the period included 263 tanks, 144 anti-tank guns, four armoured vehicles and 60 trucks.

PANTHER AUSF. D

Black 211 belonged to the 'Grossdeutschland' Panzer Division, though exactly which unit is unknown. This is how it looked at Kursk during August 1943.

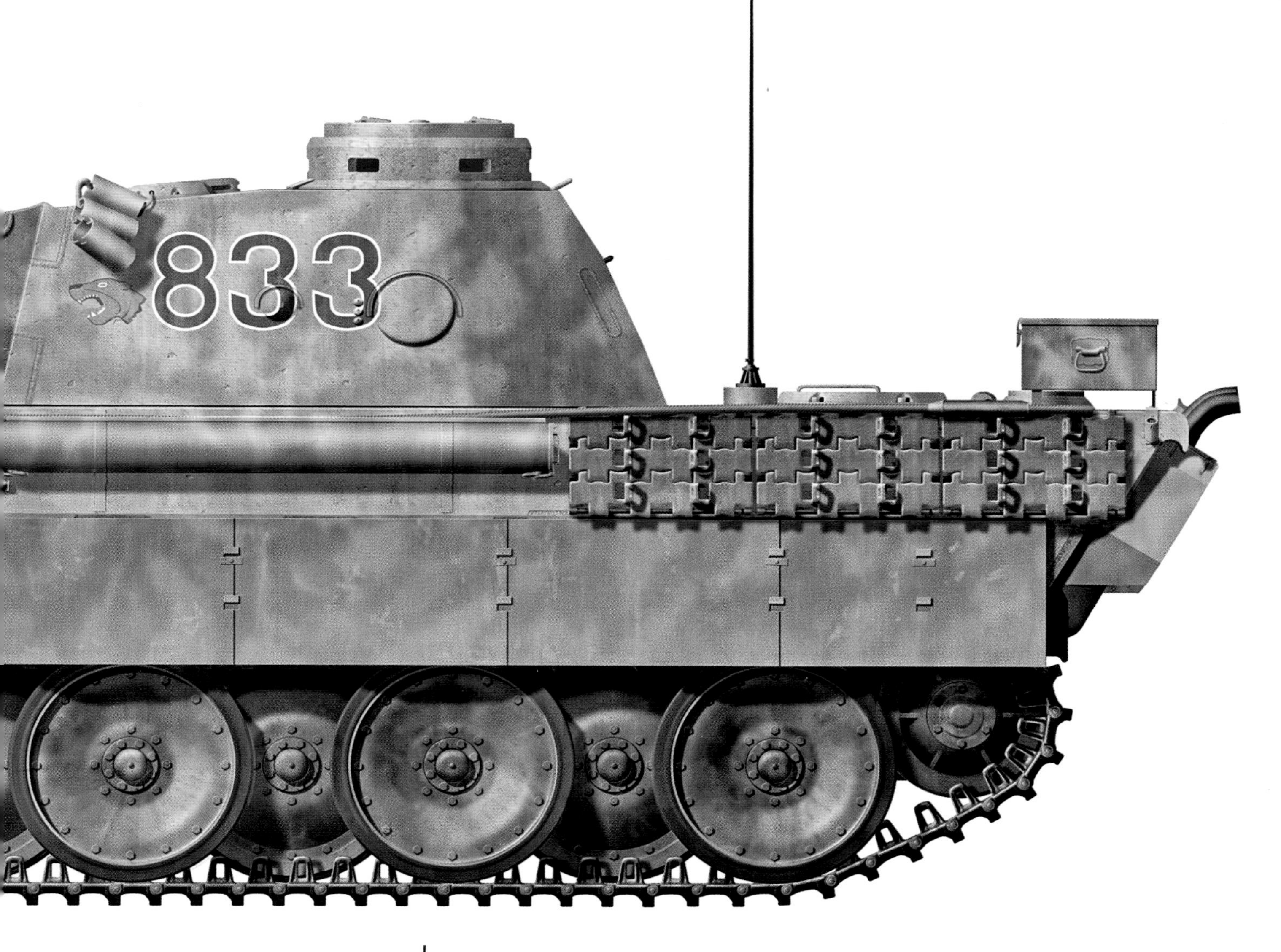

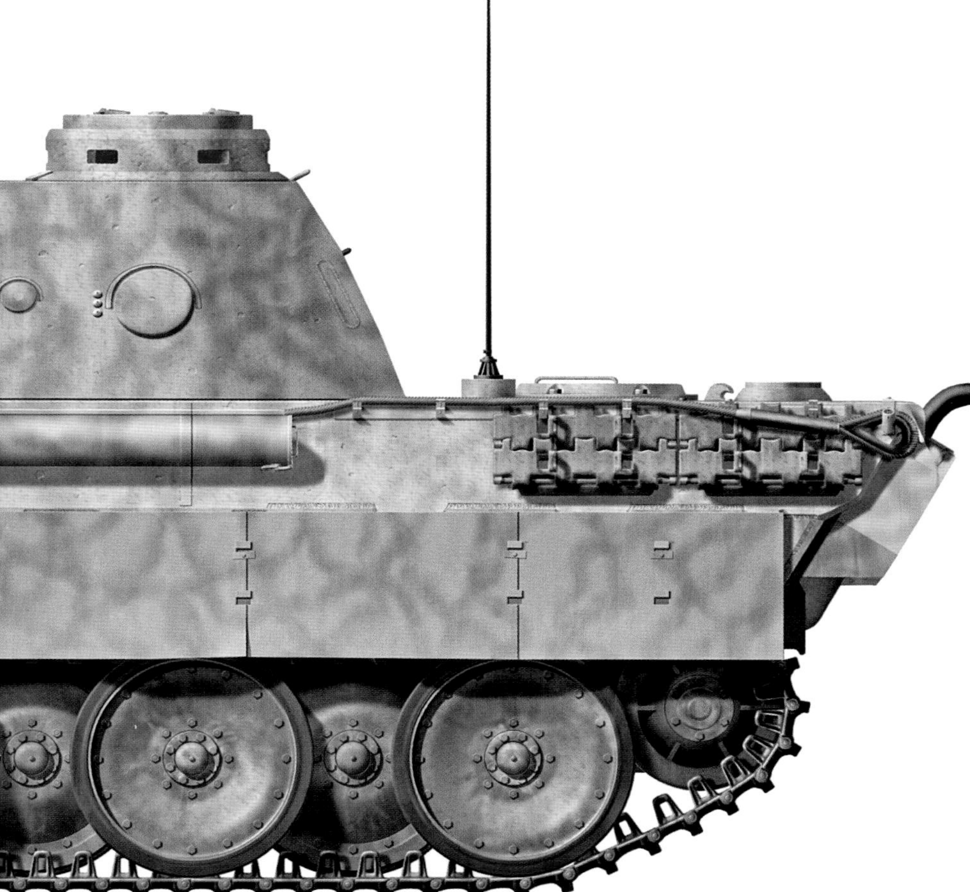

year. The result was that the new models, the Tiger and the Panther, showed many mechanical difficulties and service failures, which everybody blamed on some other firm or organisation. Many accusations of incompetence were made in secret and openly the feeling seems to have been general that the whole programme was badly handled."

A more detailed account is offered in CIOS report XXXII-2, Investigation of Tank Development (Panther) at Maschinenfabrik Augsburg & Nürnberg (MAN): "In January 1942 the OKH, as represented by [Heinrich] Kniepkamp, visited MAN requesting that a design layout be made of a tank with the following characteristics: weight 35 metric tons, speed 60km/h, armament capable of carrying a turret mounting the 75mm gun with coaxial MG. Armour thickness: hull front 60mm, hull side 40mm, hull rear 35mm, turret front 100mm, turret side 40mm. Ground pressure 0.65kg/cm2, fording depth 4m, engine Maybach HL 210.

"At about the same time Daimler-Benz, Berlin, was given the same set of characteristics and requested to submit layouts. In April 1942 the designs submitted by MAN and Daimler-Benz were reviewed by OKH [Oberkommando des Heeres – the German Army's high command]; the MAN design being chosen as the most satisfactory."

PANTHER AUSF. A

When the D-Day landings commenced, the Panzer Lehr Division was the strongest in the German Army, with 109 tanks, 40 assault guns and 612 armoured half-tracks at its disposal. This Panther, I1 of the I. Battalion of the Panzer Regiment 6, Panzer Lehr Division, was named 'Ursula'. It is shown as it appeared in Hungary during the spring of 1944 but was later featured in a Wochenschau newsreel during the Normandy battles in June-July 1944. It was finally destroyed on July 11 north of Le Dézert, northwestern France, by the US 9th Infantry Division.

The latter was designated VK 30.02 (MAN) and had little in common with the T-34 other than sloped armour plating and a long-barrelled gun, whereas Daimler-Benz produced a trio of vehicles, each slightly different from the others, which bore a much stronger resemblance to the T-34. Despite their differences these were collectively referred to as the VK 30.02 (DB).

The report continues: "MAN worked rapidly and had the first soft plate prototype ready for tests in September 1942. Tests on the first prototype were conducted by MAN at Nürnberg. The second prototype, completed shortly after the first, going to Kummersdorf. These tests showed that the HL 210 engine was not capable of delivering the desired performance as the weight of the vehicle was greater than originally specified. During these trials it was also decided to increase the frontal hull armour from 60mm to 80mm which would again

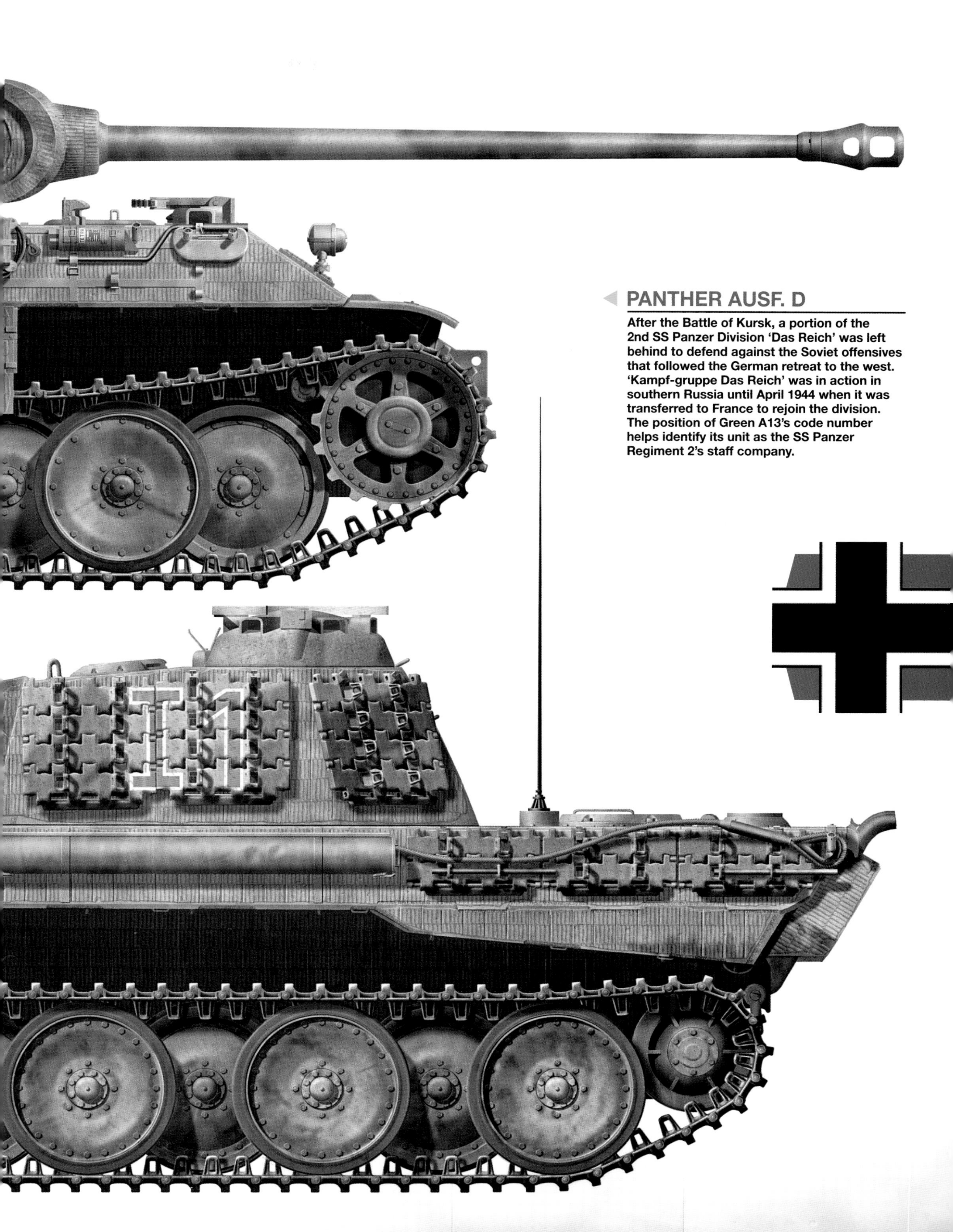

PANTHER AUSF. D

After the Battle of Kursk, a portion of the 2nd SS Panzer Division 'Das Reich' was left behind to defend against the Soviet offensives that followed the German retreat to the west. 'Kampf-gruppe Das Reich' was in action in southern Russia until April 1944 when it was transferred to France to rejoin the division. The position of Green A13's code number helps identify its unit as the SS Panzer Regiment 2's staff company.

increase the weight and necessitate the use of a larger engine to give the desired performance. As a result, the HL 230 engine was used in all production vehicles, but the first 20 Panthers had the 60mm frontal armour." In fact, the first 250 Panthers were built with the HL 210 engine.

The report goes on: "The weight of the Panther with the 80mm front hull armour and the HL 230 engine in early production had increased to 44 metric tons. Ground pressure increased to 0.85kg/cm². The track, designed by Ritsche of Hamburg, was initially 65cm wide, but because of the limitations of strategic mobility, was never increased.

"The design of the complete turret assembly and gun mount was done by Rheinmetall-Borsig (R-B) of Dusseldorf under the direction of Ing. Zimmer, chief turret designer of this firm. Close liaison with MAN was maintained, Herr Krahn being the R-B engineer at MAN ▶

THE WEIGHT OF THE PANTHER WITH THE 80MM FRONT HULL ARMOUR AND THE HL 230 ENGINE IN EARLY PRODUCTION HAD INCREASED TO 44 METRIC TONS. GROUND PRESSURE INCREASED TO 0.85KG/CM^2.

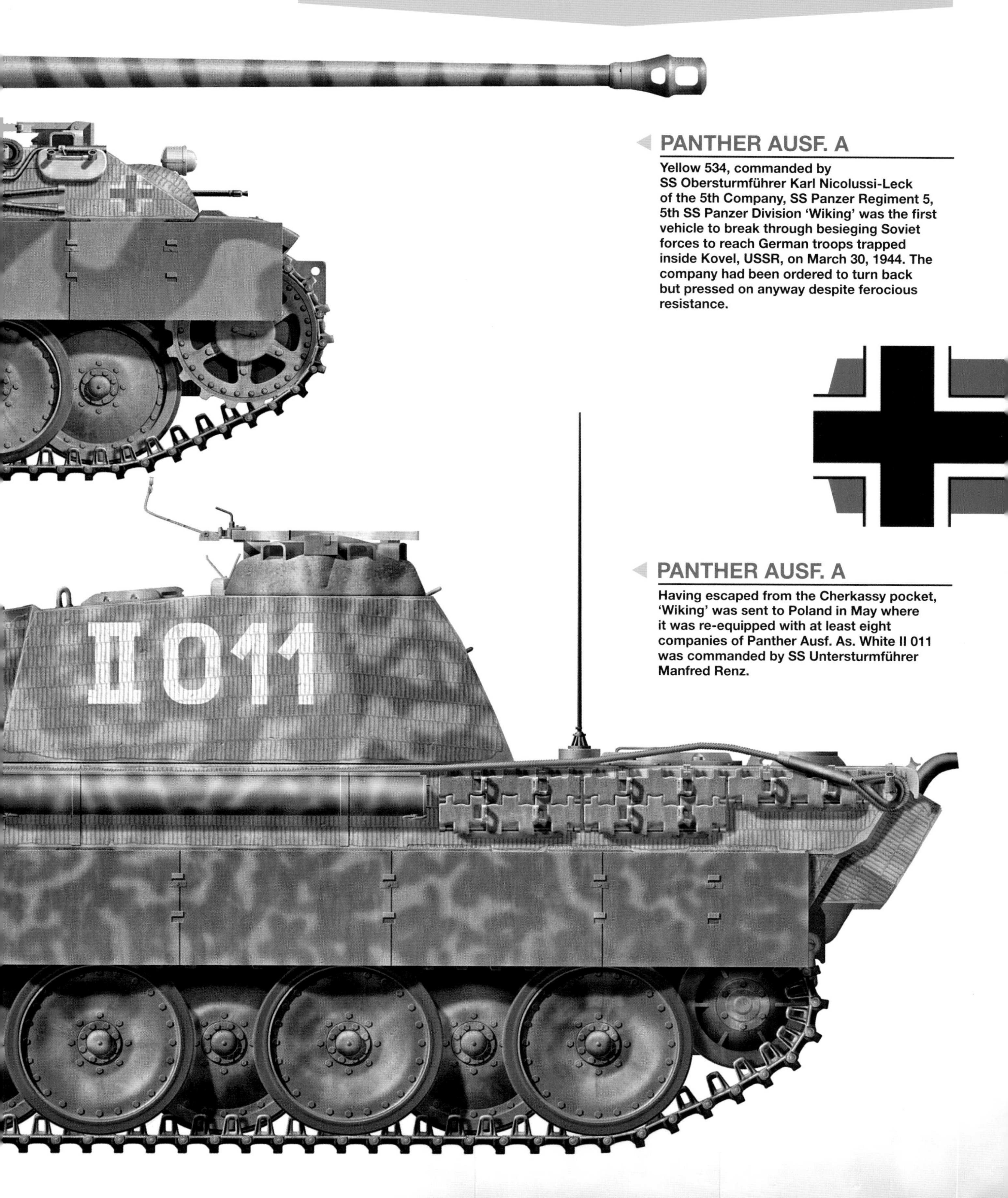

PANTHER AUSF. A

Yellow 534, commanded by SS Obersturmführer Karl Nicolussi-Leck of the 5th Company, SS Panzer Regiment 5, 5th SS Panzer Division 'Wiking' was the first vehicle to break through besieging Soviet forces to reach German troops trapped inside Kovel, USSR, on March 30, 1944. The company had been ordered to turn back but pressed on anyway despite ferocious resistance.

PANTHER AUSF. A

Having escaped from the Cherkassy pocket, 'Wiking' was sent to Poland in May where it was re-equipped with at least eight companies of Panther Ausf. As. White II 011 was commanded by SS Untersturmführer Manfred Renz.

PANTHER

PANTHER AUSF. A

SS Unterscharfuhrer Ernst Barkmann of the 4th Company, SS Panzer Regiment 2, 2nd SS Panzer Division and commander of Black 424 quickly adjusted to the conditions of Normandy and saw heavy fighting against American M4 Shermans and M5 Stuarts. He halted several major armoured thrusts and some sources claim he knocked out 15 tanks in two days during late June. Black 424 is shown as it appeared at Saint-Lô in June 1944. Overall, Barkmann is credited with more than 82 tank kills during the war, after which he worked as the fire chief but was also the mayor of his home town Kisdorf.

to take care of production changes. In production the turret body was furnished in the unfinished state to MAN by several concerns, the final machining and assembly being done by them.

"The suspension design was made by MAN and it shows the influence of Kniepkamp, who spent much time there during the construction of the prototype vehicles. The torsion bar springs, furnished by Dittman and Neuhaus in the Ruhr, were designed for 100,000lb per square inch maximum stress. Bars were not preset, as the OKH had ruled that bars were to be interchangeable right and left. Bogie wheels were furnished by Kronprinz at Solingen. Shock absorbers were furnished by Hemscheid-Wuppertal, Ruhr.

"When questioned about the responsibility for stowage of ammunition and crew duffel, since MAN had the responsibility for the chassis and R-B the responsibility for the turret assembly, Herr Wiebeche [MAN's chief engineer on the design of the Panther] stated that the OKH had designed the stowage arrangements and had furnished this information to MAN for incorporation in the production drawings.

"The requirement for provisions to allow fording 4m of water, which had been laid down in the original characteristics, had been applied in early production in an incomplete form. Due to the complication in manufacture, however, MAN was directed to

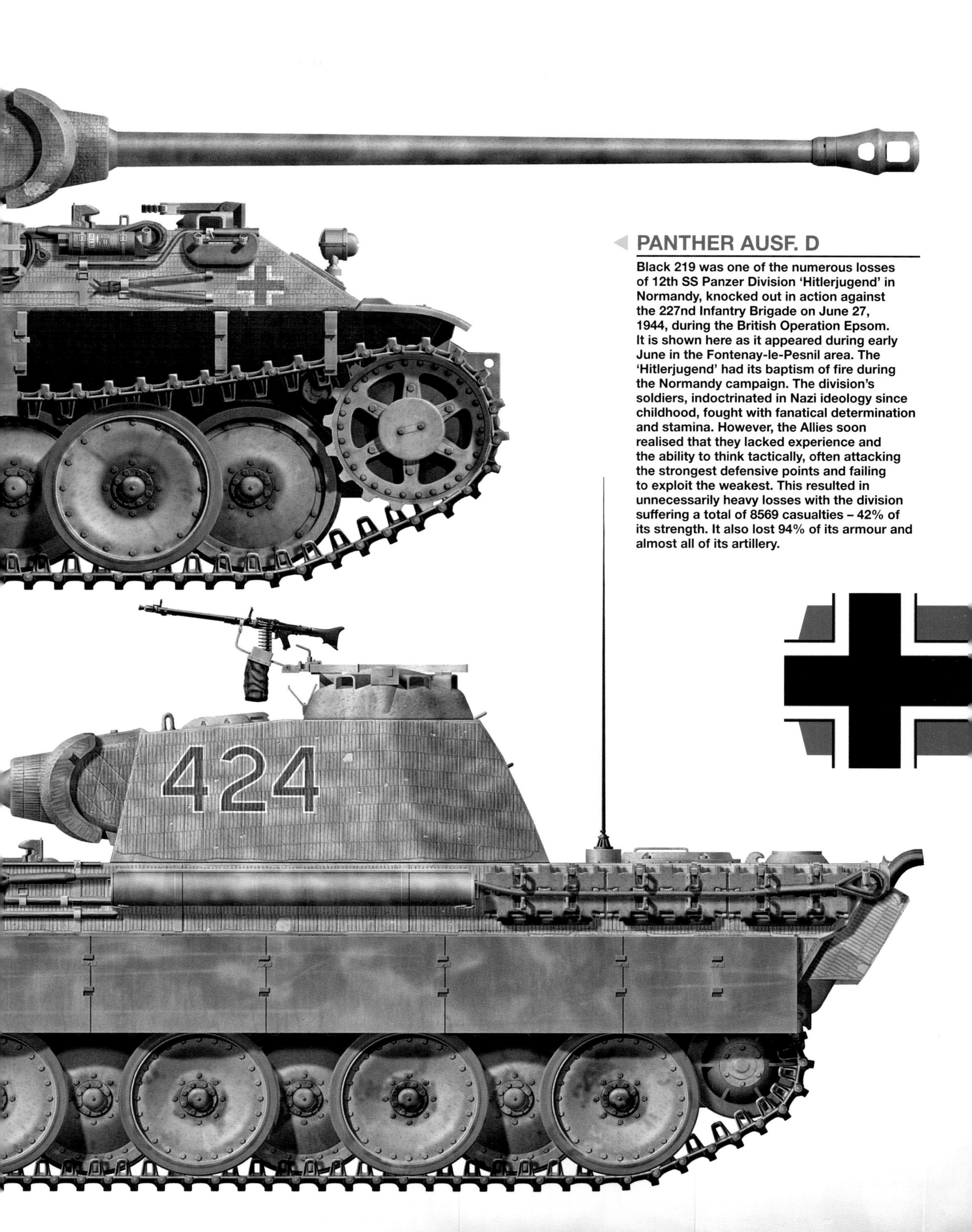

PANTHER AUSF. D

Black 219 was one of the numerous losses of 12th SS Panzer Division 'Hitlerjugend' in Normandy, knocked out in action against the 227nd Infantry Brigade on June 27, 1944, during the British Operation Epsom. It is shown here as it appeared during early June in the Fontenay-le-Pesnil area. The 'Hitlerjugend' had its baptism of fire during the Normandy campaign. The division's soldiers, indoctrinated in Nazi ideology since childhood, fought with fanatical determination and stamina. However, the Allies soon realised that they lacked experience and the ability to think tactically, often attacking the strongest defensive points and failing to exploit the weakest. This resulted in unnecessarily heavy losses with the division suffering a total of 8569 casualties – 42% of its strength. It also lost 94% of its armour and almost all of its artillery.

PANTHER

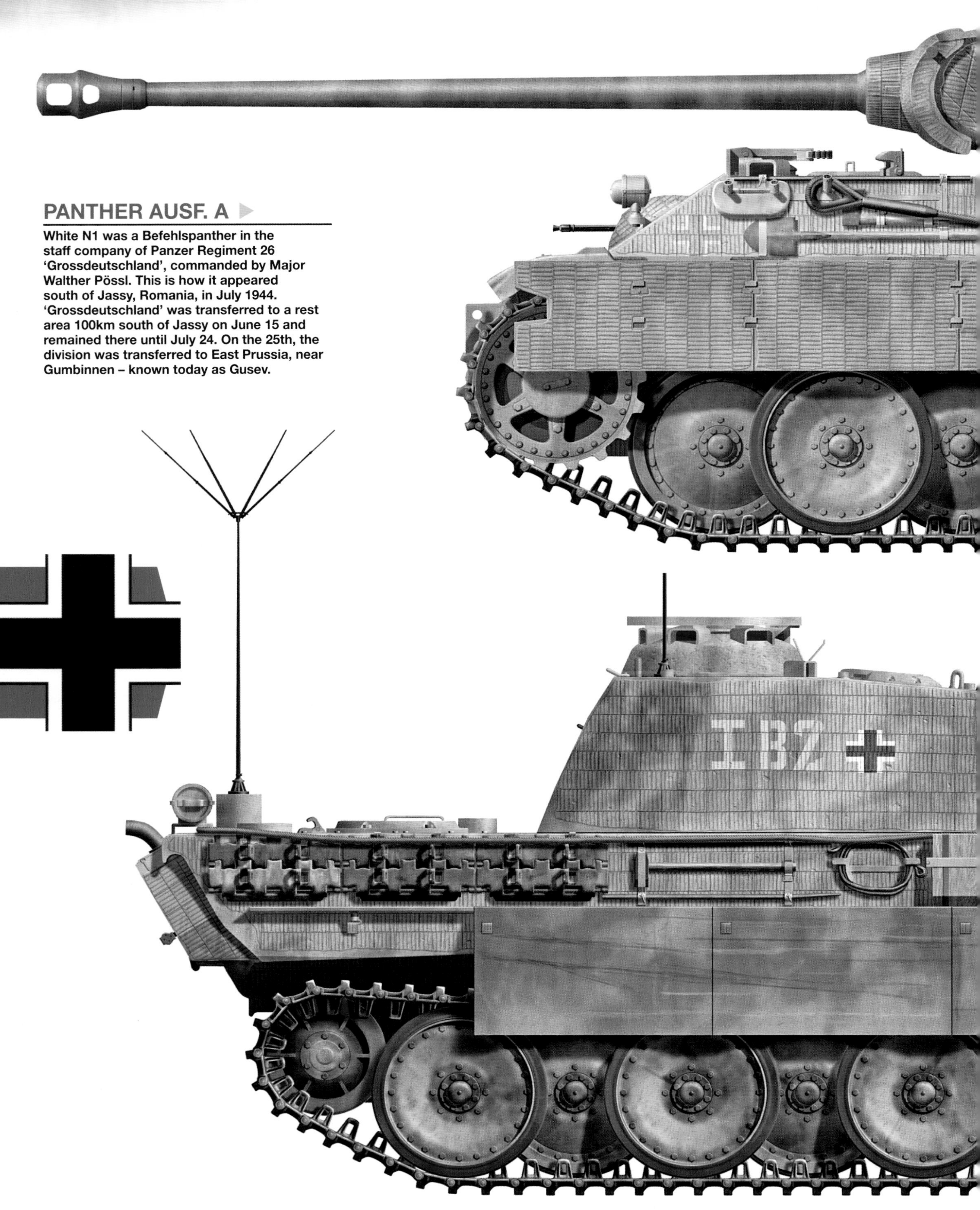

PANTHER AUSF. A

White N1 was a Befehlspanther in the staff company of Panzer Regiment 26 'Grossdeutschland', commanded by Major Walther Pössl. This is how it appeared south of Jassy, Romania, in July 1944. 'Grossdeutschland' was transferred to a rest area 100km south of Jassy on June 15 and remained there until July 24. On the 25th, the division was transferred to East Prussia, near Gumbinnen – known today as Gusev.

PANTHER AUSF. A

This is White 321 of Panzer Regiment 26's I. Battalion as it appeared in Lithuania during the summer of 1944. It was commanded by Oberfeldwebel Guth.

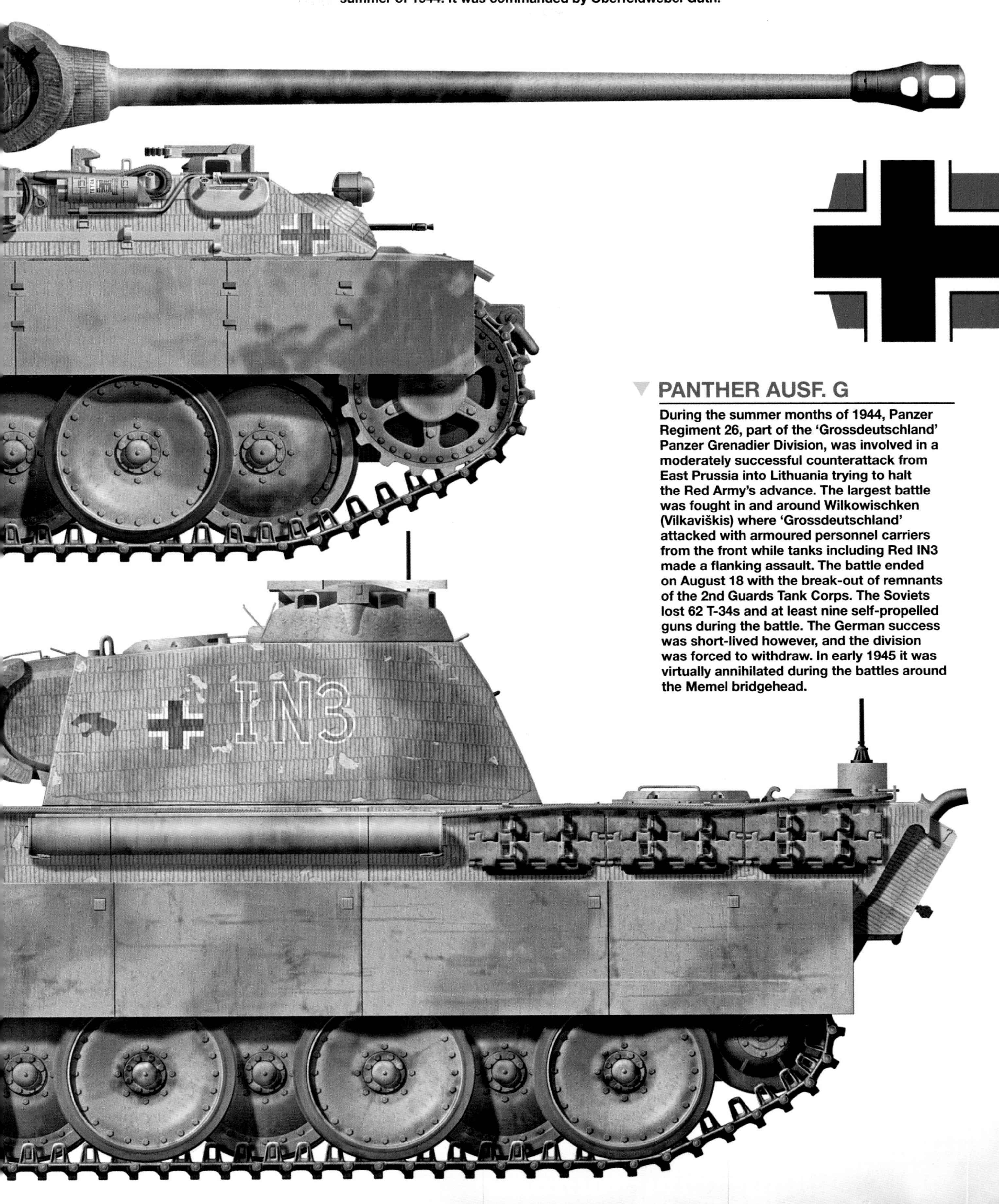

PANTHER AUSF. G

During the summer months of 1944, Panzer Regiment 26, part of the 'Grossdeutschland' Panzer Grenadier Division, was involved in a moderately successful counterattack from East Prussia into Lithuania trying to halt the Red Army's advance. The largest battle was fought in and around Wilkowischken (Vilkaviškis) where 'Grossdeutschland' attacked with armoured personnel carriers from the front while tanks including Red IN3 made a flanking assault. The battle ended on August 18 with the break-out of remnants of the 2nd Guards Tank Corps. The Soviets lost 62 T-34s and at least nine self-propelled guns during the battle. The German success was short-lived however, and the division was forced to withdraw. In early 1945 it was virtually annihilated during the battles around the Memel bridgehead.

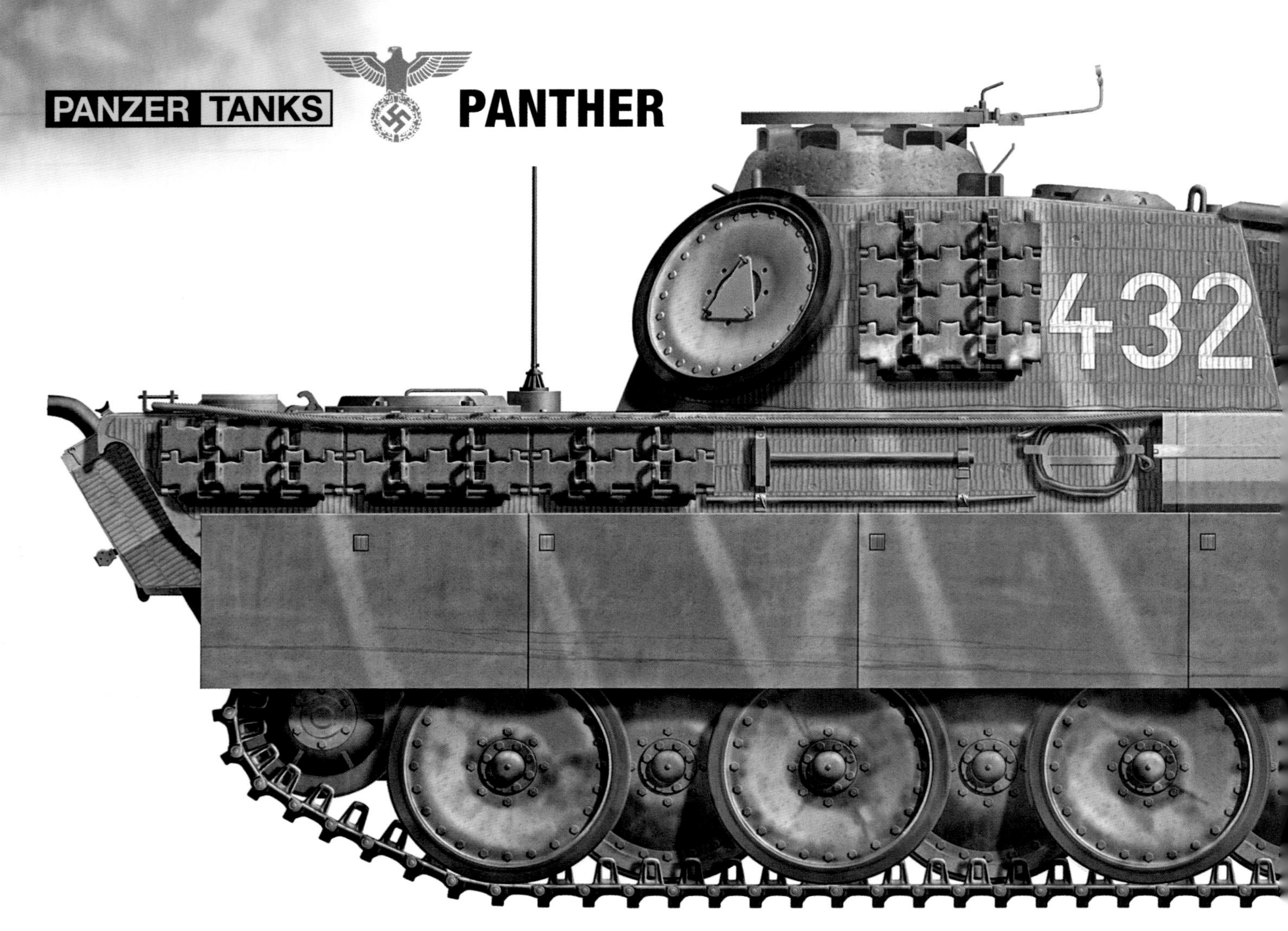

with the transmission gears due to the greater power of the HL 230 and the weight increase over that originally contemplated. MIAG at Brunswick, builders of the Jagdpanther, had developed new, stronger gears for the ZF transmission which had proven satisfactory. However, these new gears were never applied to MAN production Panthers.

"D. Differential and steering – minor troubles were experienced with this MAN designed unit, but it was considered satisfactory in that either the transmission or final drives or both would fail before failures would occur at this point. It was not regarded as satisfactory from the central standpoint, however. ▶

PANTHER AUSF. A ▶

Units of the 1st Ukrainian Front penetrated the German 4th Panzer Army's defensive line near the Polish city of Sandomierz on August 10, 1944, and by crossing the Vistula River established a large beachhead west of Baranov. The 16th Panzer Division was given the task of eliminating the bridgehead by attacking towards Pinczow. The Panthers of Panzer Regiment 2, including Black I01, were to be supported by Tiger IIs of Major von Legas from the 501st Heavy Panzer Battalion. The attack initially made good progress, despite numerous minefields, but many of the Tiger IIs soon broke down. According to Soviet reports, 14 of them were left on the battlefield. Finally, after attacking another section of the bridgehead in mid-October, the battalion was sent to the Kielce area for rest and refit. One of the Tiger IIs captured by the Red Army during this battle is now on display at the Russian AFV Museum at Kubinka.

PANTHER AUSF. G

White 432, commanded by Leutnant Weidemann, belonged to the 4th Company of the I. Battalion of Panzer Regiment 24 and is shown as it appeared at Sourdeval in Normandy, France, during August 1944 in the days before the so-called Mortain counter-offensive against US forces. Characteristic features of I./24 Panthers are the attachment of spare road wheels and tracks to the turret, striped camouflage and the positioning of the tank's numbers. The last two digits were repeated on the turret rear, and the unit's 'leaping horseman' insignia was on the left front of the glacis plate.

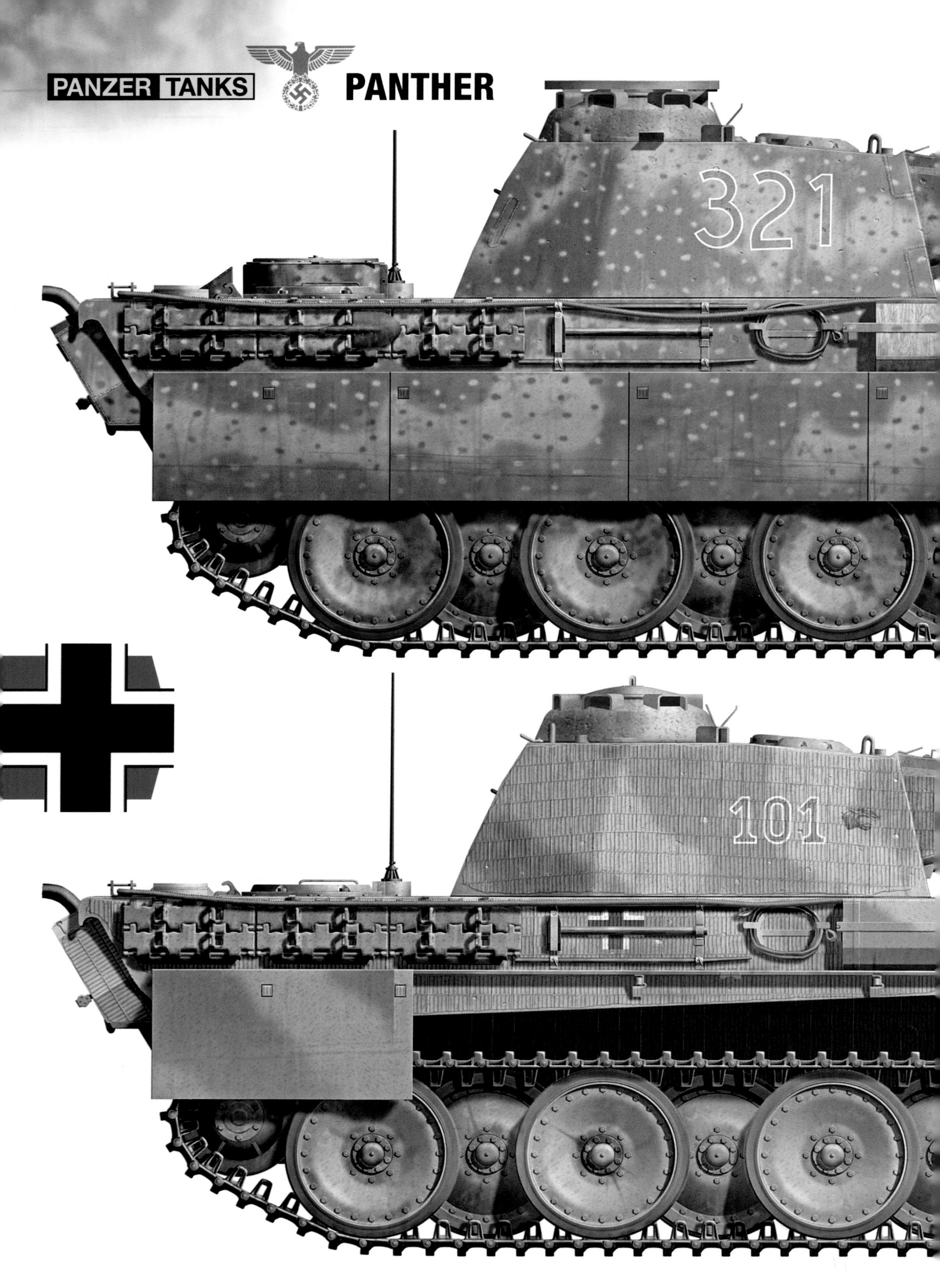
321
101

PANTHER AUSF. A

Red 321 of the 33rd Panzer Regiment was knocked out in the Falaise pocket, France, during August 1944. Between 80,000 and 100,000 German troops were caught in the Allied encirclement that followed the American breakout from the Normandy beachhead. Between 10,000 and 15,000 of them were killed and between 40,000 and 50,000 were taken prisoner. Just 20,000 to 50,000 escaped. The Allies estimated that the Germans lost around 500 tanks and assault guns as well.

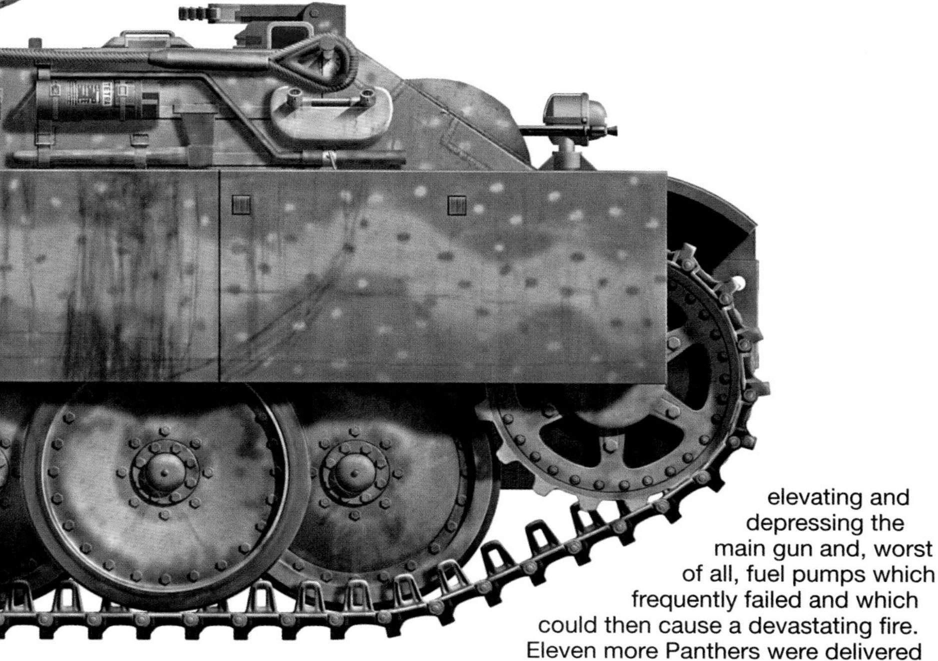

With a possible maximum speed of 45km/h, this type of steering control was not at all suitable."

Other problems with the early model Panthers included the turret sticking on hatches as it traversed, difficulty in elevating and depressing the main gun and, worst of all, fuel pumps which frequently failed and which could then cause a devastating fire.

Eleven more Panthers were delivered by MAN during February 1943, with another six being built by Daimler-Benz and one more by Maschinenfabrik Niedersachsen Hannover (MNH). These three companies built another 58 Panther Ausf. Ds during March while Henschel also contributed its first 10 Panthers.

Despite the testimony of MAN staff given to Allied interrogators, remedial work was carried out after 160 Panthers had been constructed. These vehicles were sent to Deutschen Maschinen AG (DEMAG) in Falkensee during April and May 1943 to have modifications made to their engine compartments, final drives, transmissions, steering and suspension.

The 250 HL 210-engined Panthers were ready by early May but none had yet been delivered to front line units. From the 251st example onwards, Panthers were built with the HL 230 which, although it had no effect on maximum speed, did improve acceleration at the cost of stressing the rest of the drive train. In June, Panthers had extra rivets added to their road wheels in order to strengthen them – although it evidently did not solve the problem. By the end of May, all the 250 early Ausf. Ds had been delivered to the German army along with 118 vehicles powered by the HL 230.

The German summer offensive on the Eastern Front, Operation Citadel, saw the Panther's combat debut with 200 vehicles fielded beginning on July 5, 1943. However, the tank's mechanical problems persisted throughout and after ▶

PANTHER AUSF. G

The 'Grossdeutschland' division was transferred to East Prussia in late July 1944. This is Red 101 of Panzer Regiment 26's I. Battalion, which was attached to the division during August.

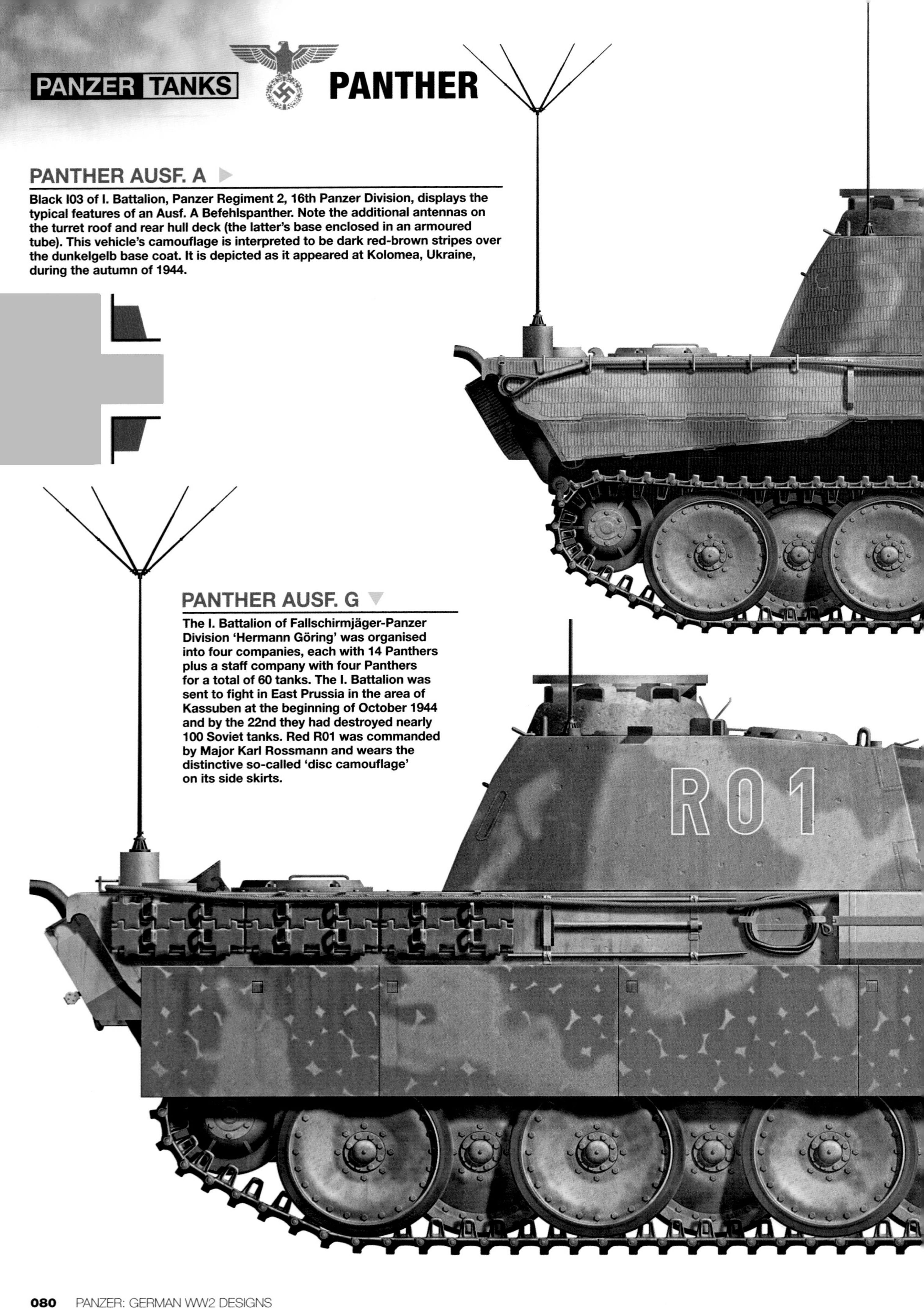

PANTHER AUSF. A

Black I03 of I. Battalion, Panzer Regiment 2, 16th Panzer Division, displays the typical features of an Ausf. A Befehlspanther. Note the additional antennas on the turret roof and rear hull deck (the latter's base enclosed in an armoured tube). This vehicle's camouflage is interpreted to be dark red-brown stripes over the dunkelgelb base coat. It is depicted as it appeared at Kolomea, Ukraine, during the autumn of 1944.

PANTHER AUSF. G

The I. Battalion of Fallschirmjäger-Panzer Division 'Hermann Göring' was organised into four companies, each with 14 Panthers plus a staff company with four Panthers for a total of 60 tanks. The I. Battalion was sent to fight in East Prussia in the area of Kassuben at the beginning of October 1944 and by the 22nd they had destroyed nearly 100 Soviet tanks. Red R01 was commanded by Major Karl Rossmann and wears the distinctive so-called 'disc camouflage' on its side skirts.

THE FIRST MAJOR CHANGE TO THE AUSF. A, IN DECEMBER 1943, WAS THE REPLACEMENT OF THE PREVIOUS NARROW SLOT FOR THE HULL MACHINE GUN WITH A BALL MOUNT WHICH OFFERED A MUCH IMPROVED FIELD OF FIRE.

three days only 40 Panthers remained operational. Three days after that, just 10 were still active.

Production changes for July included deleting the communications hatch on the left side of the turret and reducing the number of headlamps from two to just one. Road wheels now received 24 rim bolts rather than just 16 for further strengthening. Zimmerit paste was introduced during September 1943, a rain guard was fitted over the turret gunsight and improved chevron pattern tracks were fitted.

PANTHER AUSF. A

Also during September, production switched from the Panther Ausf. D to the Ausf. A. This consisted of an Ausf. D chassis fitted with an improved turret. This featured a hemispherical commander's cupola with seven periscopes, each with its own armoured cowling. It also had a ring fixture to which a machine gun could be fitted. Apart from this, the Ausf. A turret looked similar

to that of the Ausf. D externally. Inside, however, it had been given a significant redesign, including the fitment of a variable speed hydraulic traverse and a more efficient system for clearing gases from the gun.

The first three Ausf. As had been delivered by MNH in August but it was not until September that Daimler-Benz and MAN also switched to Ausf. A production. Henschel ceased to build Panthers at this point and DEMAG took over instead, although it built no more than about 50 Panthers in total before ceasing production. Between them, these four companies would build 2200 Panther Ausf. As over the course of a year – up to July 1944.

The first major change to the Ausf. A, in December 1943, was the replacement of the previous narrow slot for the hull machine gun with a ball mount which offered a much improved field of fire. The mount itself incorporated a gunsight for ▶

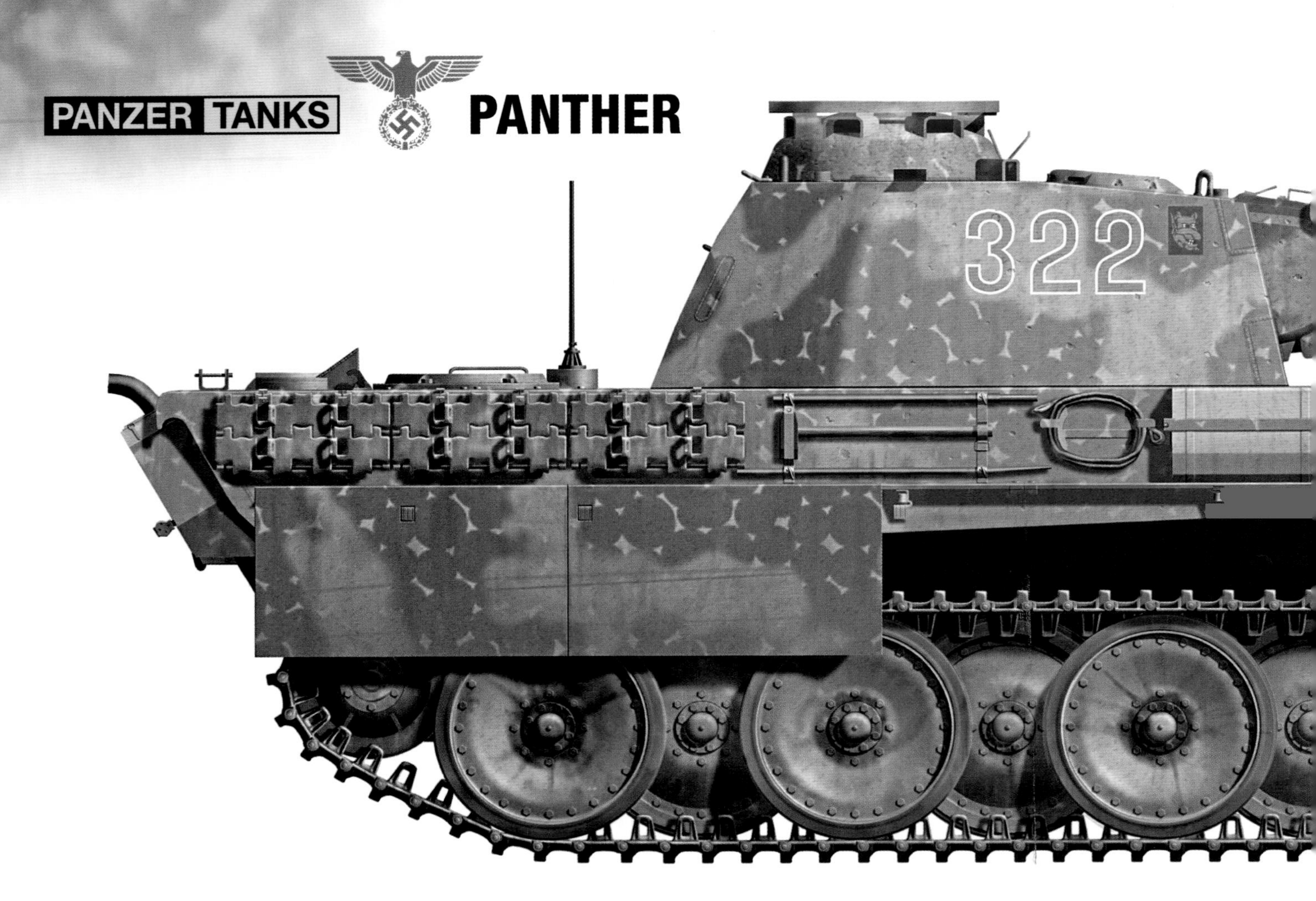

the radio operator, which allowed the original separate sight, a periscope on the upper part of the hull, to be deleted from the design. The main gunsight, formerly a TFZ 12 binocular device, was also replaced – by a TFZ 12a monocular type. At the same time, Panthers began to roll off the production line with their turret pistol ports deleted and a mount for a close defence weapon incorporated into the rear right turret roof.

The following month, new Panthers were produced with two extra cooling pipes on their left main exhaust pipe, giving it a trident-like appearance. And finally, from June to July 1944, the last Ausf. A Panthers had a trio of sockets welded to the turret roof for the fitting of a jib boom crane, which could be used to extract the vehicle's engine for maintenance or replacement.

PANTHER II

Back in January 1943, plans had been drafted to produce an up-armoured version of the Panther as the 'Panther II'. This would have been very

PANTHER AUSF. G ▶

White 212 was lost in the Sterpigny-Baclain area of Belgium during the late December battles in the Ardennes. It belonged to the 2nd Company, I. Battalion, Panzer Regiment 9, 9th SS Panzer Division 'Hohenstaufen'. By the middle of January, the division had suffered such severe losses, including 32 Panthers, that it was transferred to the reserves.

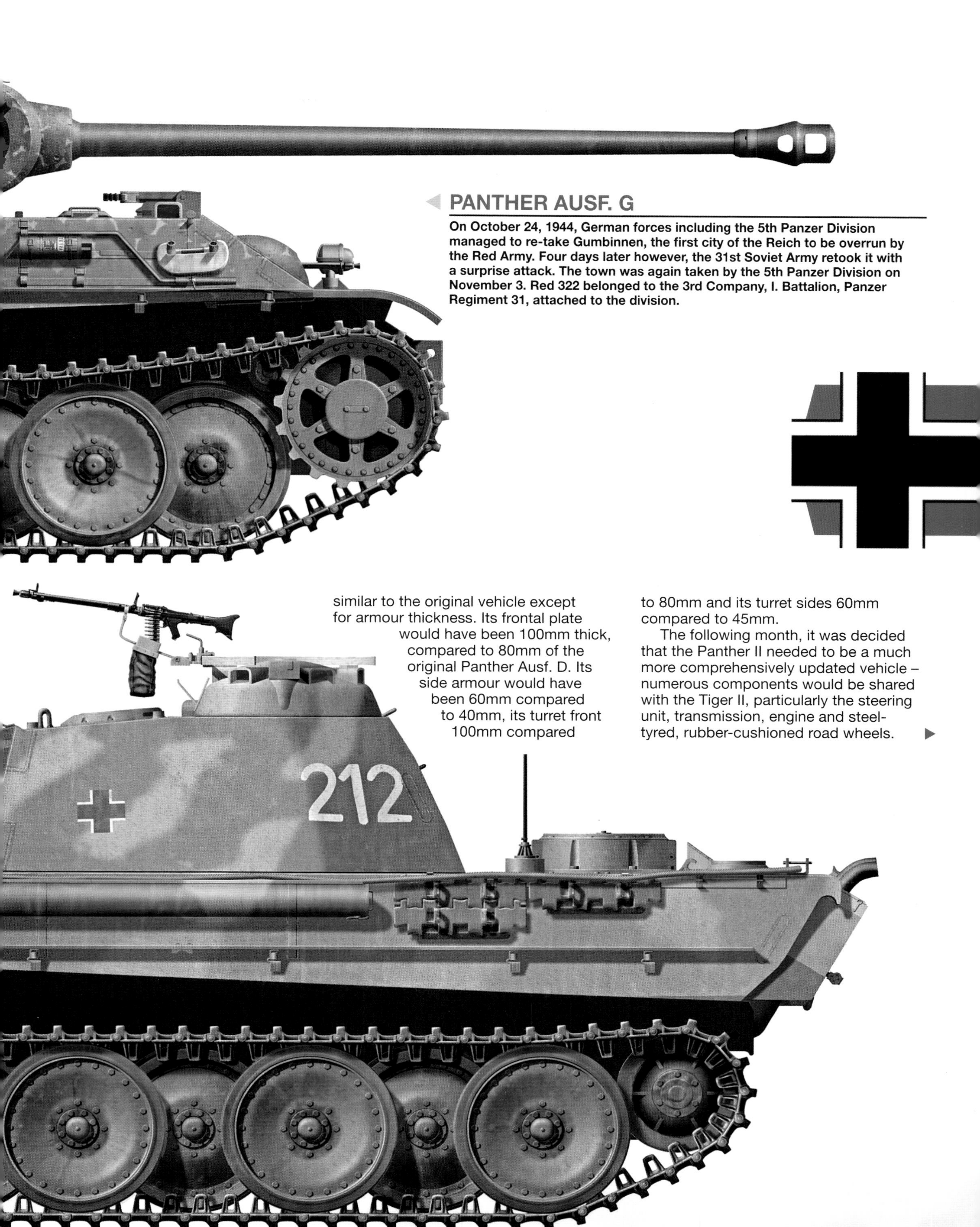

PANTHER AUSF. G

On October 24, 1944, German forces including the 5th Panzer Division managed to re-take Gumbinnen, the first city of the Reich to be overrun by the Red Army. Four days later however, the 31st Soviet Army retook it with a surprise attack. The town was again taken by the 5th Panzer Division on November 3. Red 322 belonged to the 3rd Company, I. Battalion, Panzer Regiment 31, attached to the division.

similar to the original vehicle except for armour thickness. Its frontal plate would have been 100mm thick, compared to 80mm of the original Panther Ausf. D. Its side armour would have been 60mm compared to 40mm, its turret front 100mm compared to 80mm and its turret sides 60mm compared to 45mm.

The following month, it was decided that the Panther II needed to be a much more comprehensively updated vehicle – numerous components would be shared with the Tiger II, particularly the steering unit, transmission, engine and steel-tyred, rubber-cushioned road wheels. ▶

PANTHER AUSF. G

The losses on both sides during the period from December 16-31, 1944, were enormous. The Americans lost more than 600 Shermans and 100 tank destroyers, while the Germans lost 222 tanks and 100 assault guns. White 111 of the 116th Panzer Division 'Windhund' was crossing a bridge in Houffalize when Allied bombs exploded nearby, blasting it into the Ourthe River. It was salvaged in September 1948, and is now on display in Houffalize with the turret number 401.

In addition, the Tiger II's transport tracks would be used as the Panther II's general use combat tracks. The turret-mounted MG 34 would be replaced with an MG 42.

In early 1943 it was proposed that Panther II production would begin during September of that year. At the end of March it was decided that the companies then building the original Panther would continue to do so until the end of 1944. However, a new facility, Werk Falkensee, would begin producing the Panther II in January or February 1944 and another new plant, Nibelungenwerk, during the middle of 1944.

By June 1943, however, it had become clear that the production lines then producing the original Panther could not be interrupted to provide for the introduction of a new vehicle. The new factories planned would similarly be geared up to build the original Panther, rather than the Panther II.

PANTHER AUSF. G

With the Panther II having been effectively cancelled, it was decided that some aspects of the design could be incorporated into the ongoing production of the original Panther. The most obvious change for the new Ausf. G was a 'straightening' of the hull sides. On the Ausf. A, the hull side edge was completely horizontal looking from the front of the vehicle towards the rear, where a sloping 'wedge' was added. On the Ausf. G, the entire hull side edge sloped gently from the front of the vehicle towards the rear, without the wedge.

In addition, in order to create more space inside the vehicle the hull sides were less sloped at just 29 degrees rather than the original 40. This meant that the effective thickness of the armour was reduced, so the actual thickness was increased from 40mm to 50mm – increasing the vehicle's weight by 0.3 tonnes. In order to balance out this weight gain with an equivalent weight loss, the lower front hull plate was reduced in thickness from 60mm to 50mm and the forward belly armour was reduced from 30mm to 25mm. ▶

PANTHER AUSF. G

Black 154 of the 1st Company, I. Battalion, Panzer Regiment 12, was one of 30 Panthers lost by the 'Hitlerjugend' Division in the Ardennes up to January 15, 1945. A study made by the Allies after the battle reported that the Panther losses could be broken down into the following causes: air attack 7%, armour-piercing rounds 33%, artillery 7%, abandoned by crew 42%, and unknown causes 11%.

111
154

PANTHER AUSF. G

This 'Hitlerjugend' Panther was disabled by C. Company of the 644th Tank Destroyer Battalion on the Wittfeld-Krinkelt road on December 17, 1944. It was probably hit in the drive-train which forced the driver to leave the road. The next day US troops set Black 126 on fire to create a 'scene' for the 165th Photo Company as one of the crewmembers is seen to be captured at gunpoint by Sergeant Bernard Cook from the same photo unit.

A TOTAL OF 2943 AUSF. GS ARE KNOWN TO HAVE BEEN BUILT BETWEEN MARCH 1944 AND APRIL 1945 WHEN PRODUCTION CEASED AS ALLIED FORCES OVERRAN THE FACTORIES BUILDING IT. OVERALL, IT IS THOUGHT THAT BETWEEN 5943 AND 6042 PANTHERS WERE BUILT.

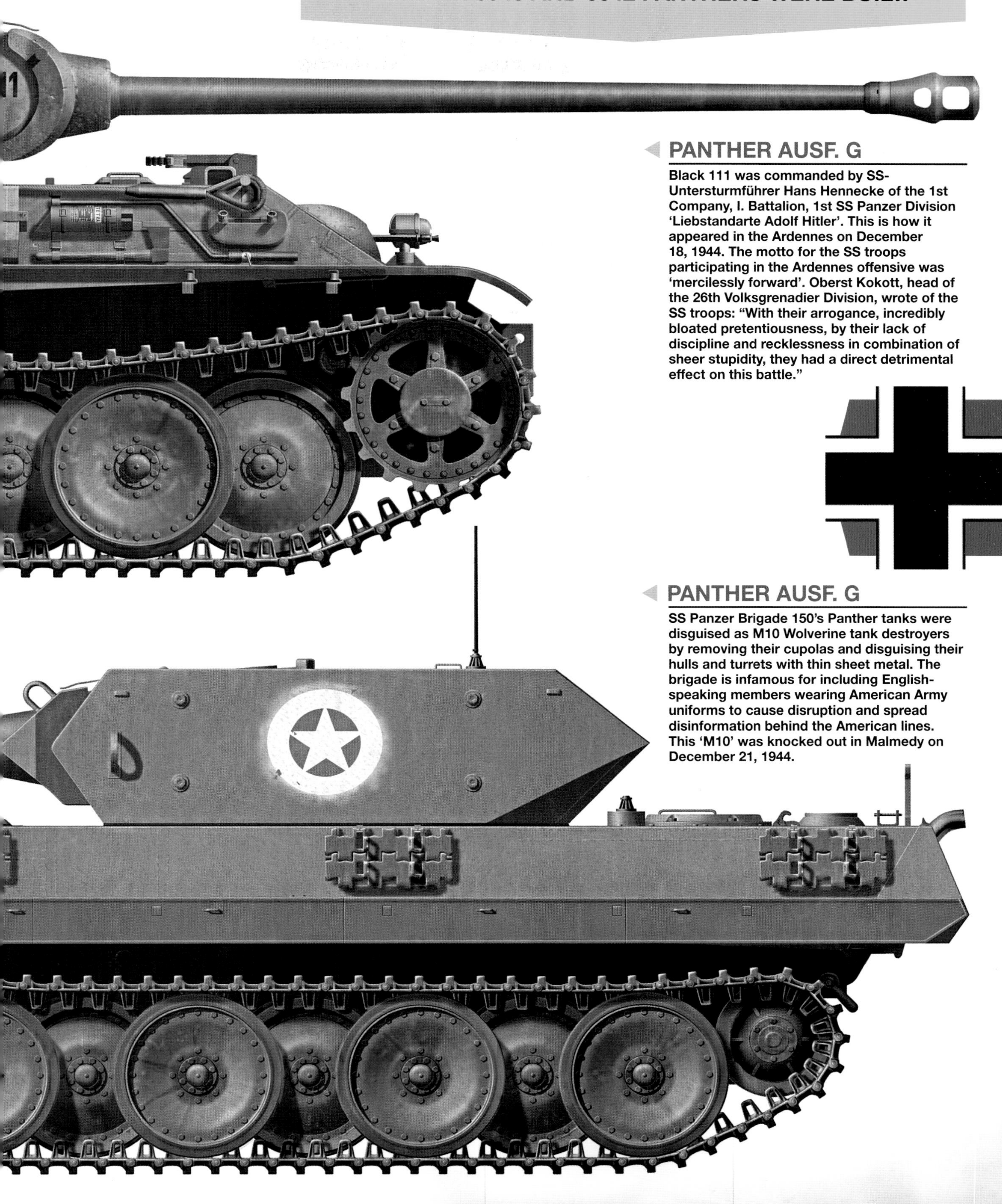

PANTHER AUSF. G

Black 111 was commanded by SS-Untersturmführer Hans Hennecke of the 1st Company, I. Battalion, 1st SS Panzer Division 'Liebstandarte Adolf Hitler'. This is how it appeared in the Ardennes on December 18, 1944. The motto for the SS troops participating in the Ardennes offensive was 'mercilessly forward'. Oberst Kokott, head of the 26th Volksgrenadier Division, wrote of the SS troops: "With their arrogance, incredibly bloated pretentiousness, by their lack of discipline and recklessness in combination of sheer stupidity, they had a direct detrimental effect on this battle."

PANTHER AUSF. G

SS Panzer Brigade 150's Panther tanks were disguised as M10 Wolverine tank destroyers by removing their cupolas and disguising their hulls and turrets with thin sheet metal. The brigade is infamous for including English-speaking members wearing American Army uniforms to cause disruption and spread disinformation behind the American lines. This 'M10' was knocked out in Malmedy on December 21, 1944.

PANTHER

PANTHER AUSF. G

Facing strong US forces, having run out of supplies and having lost contact with the German units behind him, Joachim Peiper, leader of 'SS-Kampfgruppe Peiper' decided on Christmas Eve 1944 to abandon his vehicles at La Gleize, Ardennes, Belgium, and escape through the woods with his 800 men on foot. Thirty-six hours later, having covered 20km through deep snow and in freezing temperatures, Peiper and his remaining 770 men finally reached the German front line. Black 221, commanded by SS-Hauptscharführer Heinz Knappich, was left behind in La Gleize.

Supreme Army Headquarters, Wa Pruf 6 Pz II. These specifications could be listed according to the following general requirements: a) the penetration of bullets under the semi-circular mounting should be prevented; b) armour reinforcement should be obtained without an increase in weight; c) a reduction in the area of impact should be obtained without a reduction in the size of the fighting compartment; d) a horizontal stereoscopic rangefinder should be installed; e) provisions should be made for the mounting of an MG 42 machine gun; f) the design should be such as to reduce the cost; and finally the fighting unit must be so constructed that through the installation of additional fittings it is possible to convert it in the shortest possible time into a commander's or FG vehicle."

This was quite a tall order but Daimler-Benz, though not renowned as a maker of turrets, managed to meet all the requirements. The report continues: "The important differences of the new turret can be recognised from the requirements given above and can be met through the following alterations: Through the development of the new 75mm KwK 44/1 gun, in which design the recuperator and buffer cylinders are situated underneath the gun, it was possible to replace the semi-circular mounting with a simple potmantle.

"Through the new mantlet the complicated welded cradle for the barrel is eliminated. The compressor equipment for the barrel blow-out appliance is eliminated. The necessary compressed air is obtained through an additional cylinder around the air recuperator utilising the recoil of about 420mm. The muzzle brake is eliminated, and the recoil force is increased from 12 to 18 tons. Through the choice of the new mantlet, the requirement of point a) in the first paragraph is met.

"Turret: The front armour of the turret could be made much ▶

PANTHER AUSF. G

When 'Kampfgruppe Bayer', part of the 116th Panzer Division 'Windhund', was surrounded by superior American forces at Verdenne, its commander Oberst Johannes Bayer had no option but to order a break-out attempt to reach German lines. This was accomplished during the night of December 27, 1944. Of the 17 Panthers and seven Panzer IVs the 116th had on hand when the Ardennes offensive commenced, only nine Panthers survived the fighting. This meant the end of 'Windhund's' offensive capacity in Ardennes, as the US Tactical Air Force made it impossible for any reinforcements to arrive. This unnumbered Panther was one of the eight lost during the offensive.

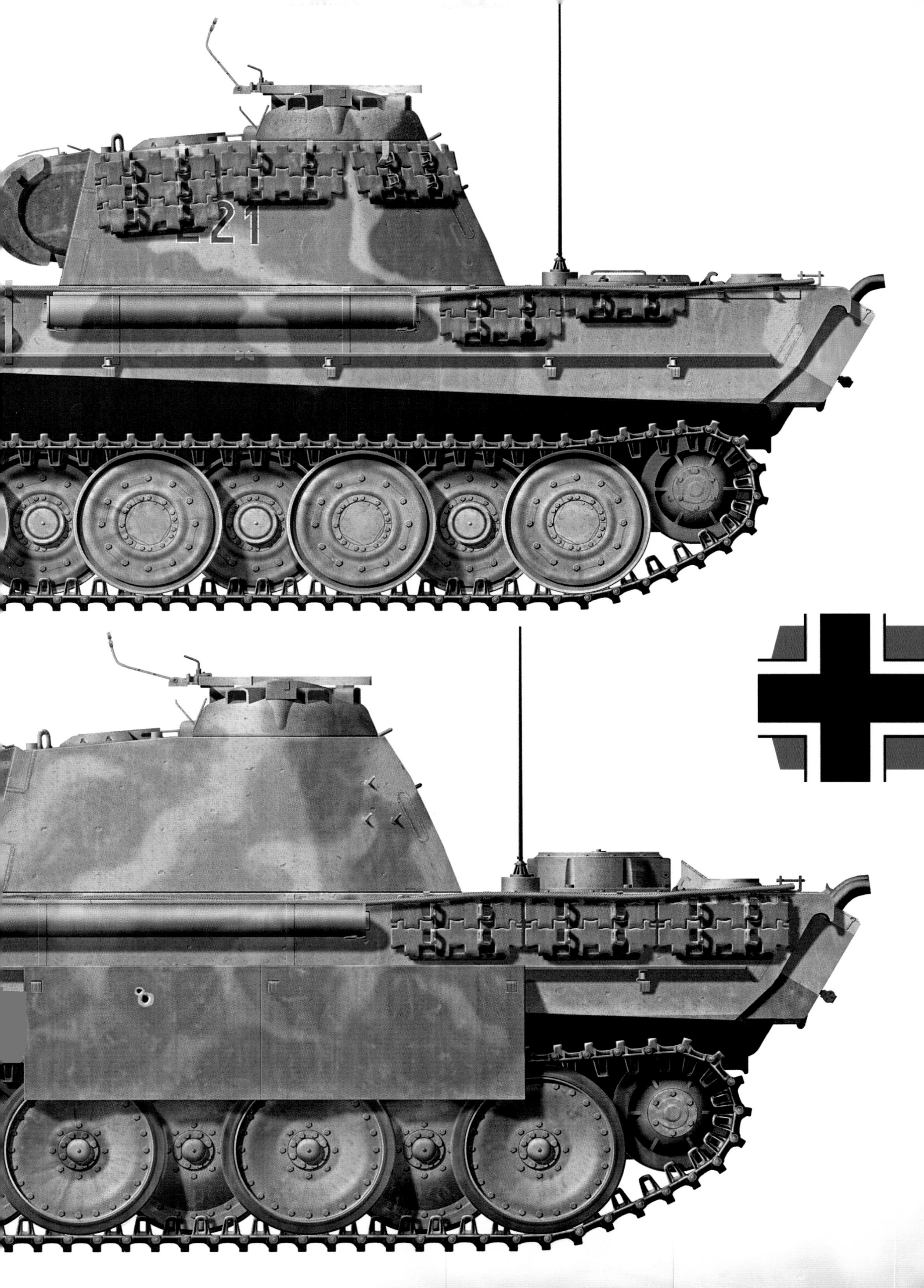
221

smaller, due to the new mantlet, and thus the impact surface was reduced. Previously this plate was made of armour steel casting with expensive mechanical machining, but this could be replaced by a homogeneous armour plate with simple mechanical machining. Through the reduction of the front plate and the choice of the new mantle, the weight was reduced so that the armour could be increased without exceeding the weight of the old turret."

The Schmalturm's small front plate was made 120mm thick, an increase of 40mm over the original design. The side plates were 60mm, up 20mm. The rear was 60mm compared to 45mm before, and the roof plate was 30mm compared to the original's 12mm.

However the report goes on to say: "The drawings specify lighter armour plate, because as a result of military events, the German steel industry was not able to produce the required amounts of rolling mill products. Installed in the turret are: one close combat weapon on the right rear of the turret roof, one commander's cupola on the left of the turret roof, one automatic pistol opening in the rear turret plate, one range finder in the front underneath the roof plate. The episcope mounting for the loader is eliminated.

"Turret ball bearing: This is a thrust bearing type with the same inside diameter as the turret interior dimension. The upper race, in addition to acting as the bearing race, forms the turret traversing rack for the power traverse. The former type of separate traversing rack is eliminated. ▶

THE SCHMALTURM'S SMALL FRONT PLATE WAS MADE 120MM THICK, AN INCREASE OF 40MM OVER THE ORIGINAL DESIGN. THE SIDE PLATES WERE 60MM, UP 20MM. THE REAR WAS 60MM COMPARED TO 45MM BEFORE, AND THE ROOF PLATE WAS 30MM COMPARED TO THE ORIGINAL'S 12MM.

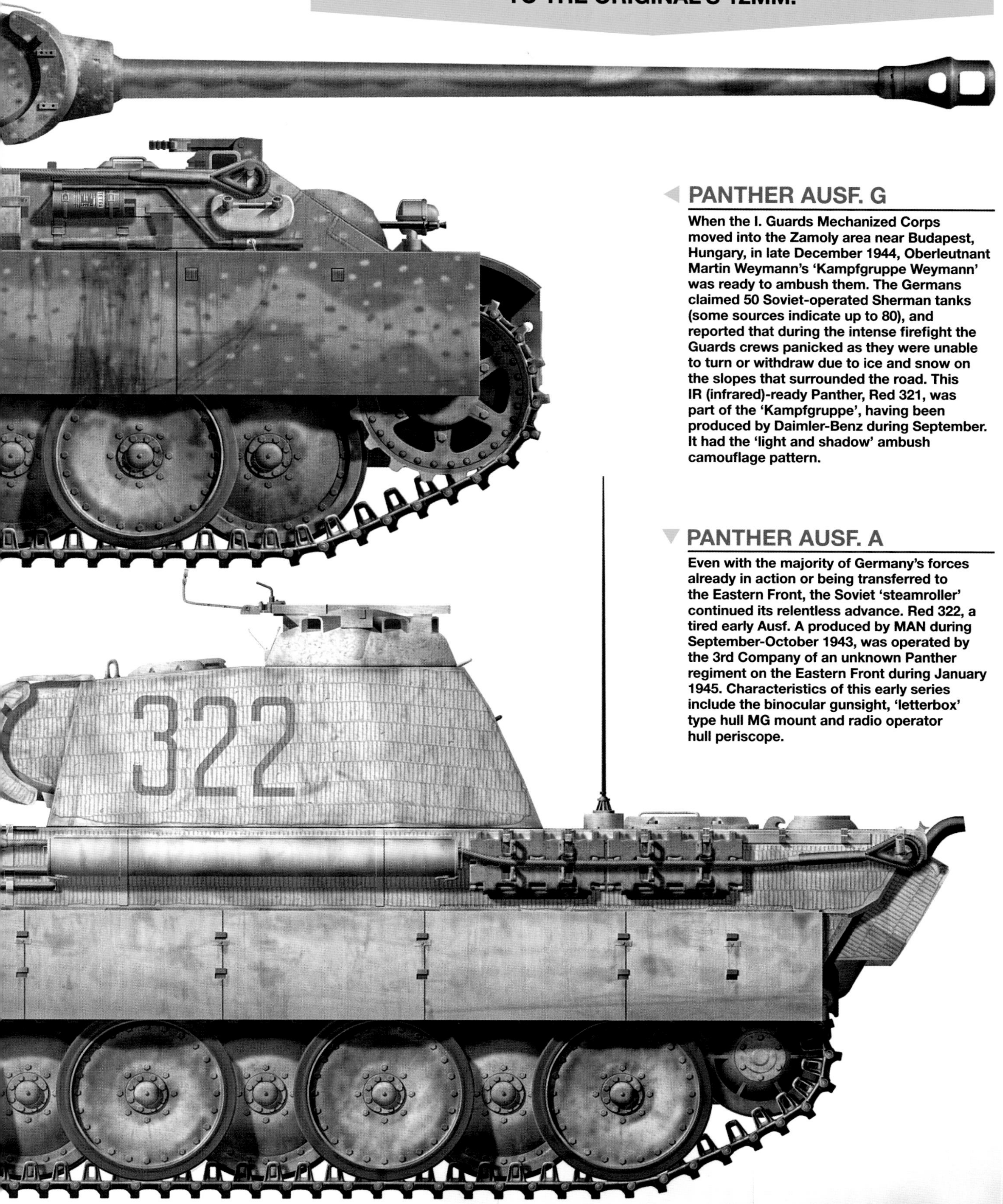

PANTHER AUSF. G

When the I. Guards Mechanized Corps moved into the Zamoly area near Budapest, Hungary, in late December 1944, Oberleutnant Martin Weymann's 'Kampfgruppe Weymann' was ready to ambush them. The Germans claimed 50 Soviet-operated Sherman tanks (some sources indicate up to 80), and reported that during the intense firefight the Guards crews panicked as they were unable to turn or withdraw due to ice and snow on the slopes that surrounded the road. This IR (infrared)-ready Panther, Red 321, was part of the 'Kampfgruppe', having been produced by Daimler-Benz during September. It had the 'light and shadow' ambush camouflage pattern.

PANTHER AUSF. A

Even with the majority of Germany's forces already in action or being transferred to the Eastern Front, the Soviet 'steamroller' continued its relentless advance. Red 322, a tired early Ausf. A produced by MAN during September-October 1943, was operated by the 3rd Company of an unknown Panther regiment on the Eastern Front during January 1945. Characteristics of this early series include the binocular gunsight, 'letterbox' type hull MG mount and radio operator hull periscope.

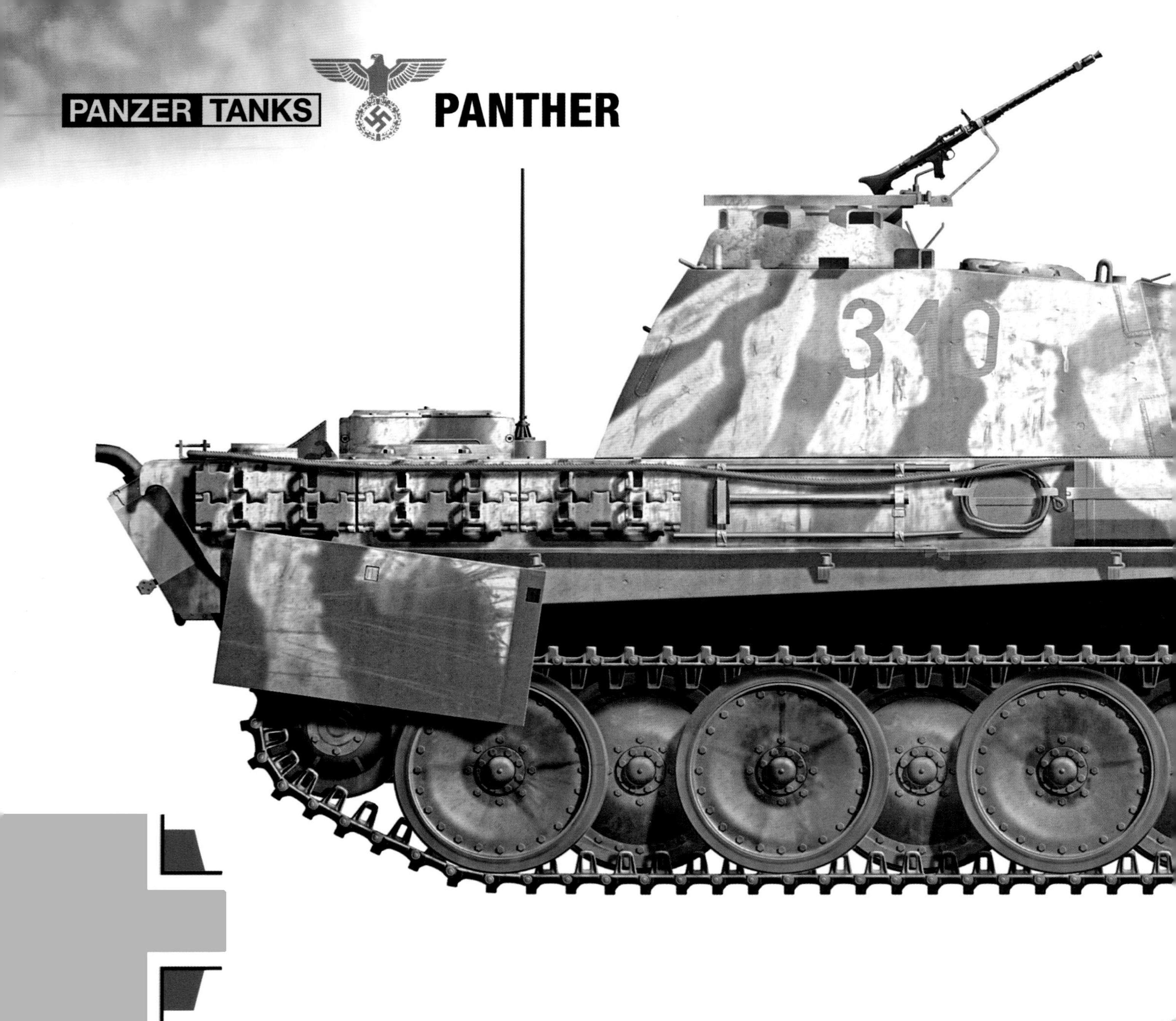

"Power traverse: The turret is traversed through a hydraulic motor fitted to the turret reinforcing ring. The traversing as well as the exact aiming is done hydraulically. For accurate control of the traverse, the former foot control is replaced by a hand control. If engine troubles occur or the hydraulic system is put out of operation, the turret can be traversed by hand. If the tank is tilted to any great degree the additional required force can be obtained through an auxiliary drive operated by the loader. The former separated drive for this auxiliary unit is eliminated."

In summary, the report notes that: "through the adaptation of these new ideas, the production time for the turret construction, excluding the manufacture of the sighting telescope, range finders, gun, etc. was reduced by 30-40%. In spite of armour up to 50% heavier, the original weight of the turret (approximately eight tons) was not exceeded.

"The surface of impact has been considerably lessened without reducing the inside space. The inside diameter of the turret of 1650mm was not altered. In the design of the new turret, the deficiencies encountered previously were either eliminated or reduced in effect: a) The penetration of bullets under the semi-circular mounting whereby the deflected bullet had often broken through the cover plates of the vehicle. b) Insufficient armour. c) Too large a surface of impact. d) Elimination of fumes from the interior of the fighting compartment. e) Costly production.

PANTHER AUSF. G

Red 310 was operated by the 'Grossdeutschland' during the Soviet land blockade of Memel, Lithuania, during January 1945. The remaining German civilians and the military wounded were evacuated by sea, followed by 'Grossdeutschland' and the 7th Panzer Division, which had both suffered heavy losses. They were replaced by the 95th Infantry Division, which arrived by ship.

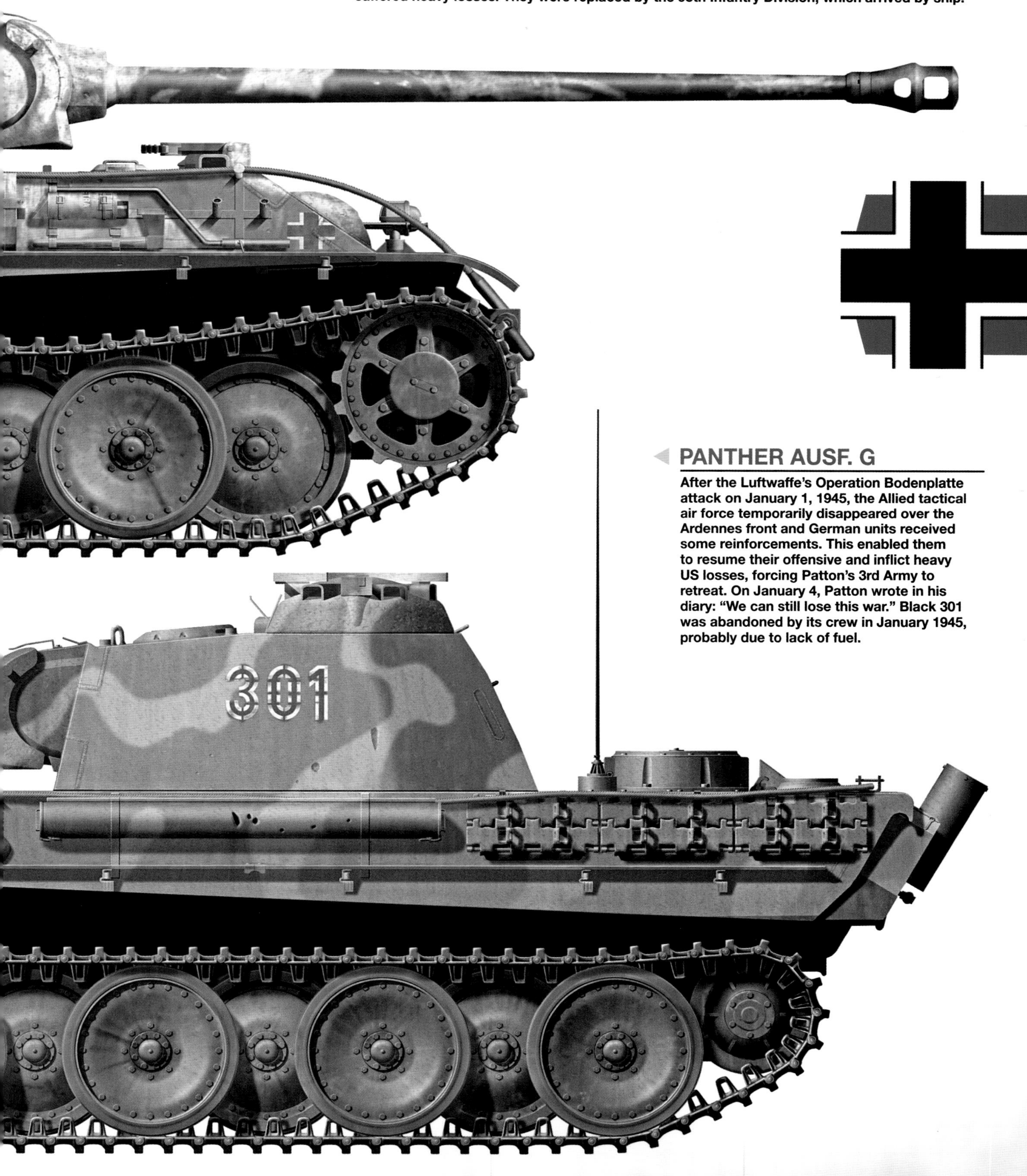

PANTHER AUSF. G

After the Luftwaffe's Operation Bodenplatte attack on January 1, 1945, the Allied tactical air force temporarily disappeared over the Ardennes front and German units received some reinforcements. This enabled them to resume their offensive and inflict heavy US losses, forcing Patton's 3rd Army to retreat. On January 4, Patton wrote in his diary: "We can still lose this war." Black 301 was abandoned by its crew in January 1945, probably due to lack of fuel.

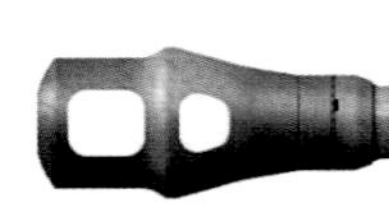

It was further planned that in the development of this turret, provision be made for the mounting of an 88mm gun and a stabilised sight."

Beyond the turret, there were other differences between the Panther F and G. The hull roof armour went from 12mm to 25mm, the hatch design modifications made to the Ausf. G for the driver and radio operator were further improved and the MG 34 mount on the front hull was to be replaced with a mount for an MG 44.

PANTHER INTO 1945

According to CIOS report XXXII-2, further upgrades to the Panther had been planned even as the end of the war approached. It states: "A programme had been set up in late 1944 by the OKH for improvements in the Panther which were to be incorporated into production as rapidly as possible. In some instances the time at which these changes were to be made was dependent upon the successful completion of design of a certain component. This was the case with the programme on air-cooled diesel engines. The following is a listing of the proposed changes, all of which were to be incorporated by the end of 1945 or early 1946.

"A. New transmission gears – the design of gears as used by MIAG in the Jagdpanther were to be used in the MAN and Daimler-Benz Panther.

"B. New bogie wheels – a new design of bogie wheel known

PANTHER AUSF. G

White 533 of the Panzer Lehr Division II. Battalion's 5th Company was damaged by a mine in Leffe, east of Bastogne, Belgium, on January 3, 1945. It was left behind during the German retreat, one of six lost during the battle.

as the 'silent bloc' type where two cushions of rubber separated the wheel disc from the steel rim, had been produced for test. Preliminary results of the testing indicated a much better life than the former bogie wheel. (This same design wheel was built for use on the E-100).

"C. New steering mechanism – MAN had been doing some development work on two types of steering mechanisms for the Panther. The first type employed electro-magnetic clutches and brakes to replace the friction clutches and brakes. The second type utilised a hydraulic system, which only functioned when the tank was steered. Very few details of this unit were known by the ▶

PANTHER AUSF. G

Yet another Panther tank lost during the battle of the Ardennes was Red 302 of the 'Windhund' at Houffalize during January 1945. German losses during the battle amounted to 370 tanks and 180 assault guns. Exact US Army tank losses will never be known as the records were destroyed after the war.

PANTHER

PANTHER AUSF. G

Up until the middle of January 1945, the 'Hermann Göring' Panzer Division fought in East Prussia in the area to the west of Gumbinnen at Insterburg. Thereafter the unit was transported back to the eastern part of Germany for refit. In February, while in Königsbrück, the 1st Company received 10 new Panther tanks, including Red 111, along with much needed replacement personnel.

PANTHER AUSF. G

Red 242 of the 19th Panzer Division was lost in the fighting in the Silesia region between April 15 and April 17, probably being abandoned due to mechanical problems or when it ran out of fuel. Later it was captured intact by the 1st Czech Independent Tank Brigade north of the Opava River.

PANTHER AUSF. G

The Panzer Division 'Feldherrnhalle 2' was created on March 23, 1945, by renaming the 13th Panzer Division, which was almost wiped out during the battle for Budapest. The formation took place in Czechoslovakia under extreme conditions with the unit being under attack by the Soviet troops in the area. Here the unit joined up with the 8th Army, and fought its only battles, in Slovakia and the upper Danube with a complement of 19 Panthers, including White 209, and 21 Panzer IVs. Its last battle was fought in the Frainspitz-Socherl area where the remains of the division managed to prevent a Soviet breakthrough. Finally, it surrendered to American troops on May 8. It was one of the few units fighting on the Eastern Front that was not handed over into Russian captivity by the US Army.

personnel interrogated, but Dr. Rathje stated that two units had been built and installed, one tested extensively in the vehicle, and the second removed for laboratory tests at MAN, Augsburg. When questioned about the power losses of such a system, Dr Rathje quickly stated that the efficiency of this mechanism was much better than the standard steering unit.

"Herr Kriebel was quite enthusiastic about the ease of control of this mechanism stating that the tank could be controlled very easily and accurately by means of a steering wheel. A search is being made for the two units, as well as the drawings of this mechanism by OTIT. MAN was quite satisfied that this mechanism was designed satisfactorily from a performance standpoint, but had redesigned the unit for production and serviceability. No production units had been produced.

"D. New turret – Daimler-Benz, Berlin, were cooperating with the Rheinmetall-Borsig on the design of a new turret patterned after the Tiger II turret, but without the large rear bulge. This turret was to be capable of mounting the 88mm gun, as well as the 75mm. Personnel of MAN know little of the details of the turret, as apparently the design had not progressed much further than the layout and discussion stage."

This appears to be a reference to the Schmalturm.

The report goes on: "E. Heaters for crew compartment – heaters were to be installed in the crew compartment to enable the crew to function more efficiently in cold weather.

"F. Air-cooled diesel engines – three designs of air-cooled diesel engines of approximately 800hp were being studied for use in the Panther. Of these three designs, the first two had progressed to the state where plans were laid for the production of a small series of vehicles ▶

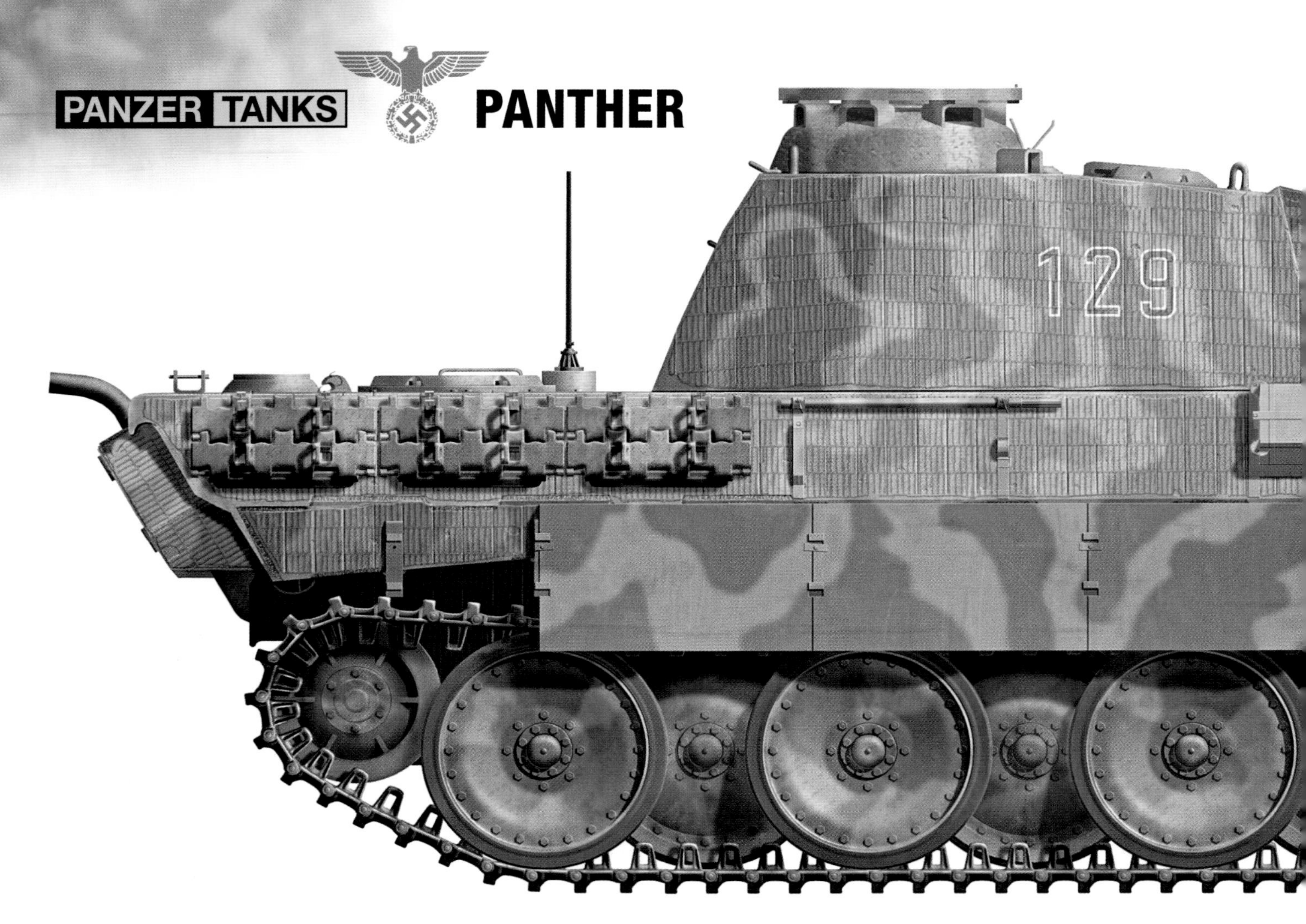

with each engine. The engines were as follows: 1. MAN-Argus – MAN and Argus, Berlin, had collaborated on the design of an air-cooled diesel, a model of which was reported to be at a dispersal point. Dr Rothman, chief engine designer of MAN, Nurnberg, was not available for questioning at the time this investigation was made. 2. Simmering – Vienna. 3. Sauer – Vienna. The Klockner-Humboldt-Deutz V8 liquid-cooled diesel engine was being considered also but had progressed only as far as the layout stage.

"When questioned about the Maybach diesel adaptation of the HL 234, Herr Wiebeche stated that Maybach had always been very optimistic about the performance of their engine, and to the best of his knowledge, the diesel version of the HL 234, as well as the HL 234, were not sufficiently developed to be placed in production. Apparently the OKH was very anxious to get the HL 234 to give more power for the Tiger II,

PANTHER AUSF. A

There has been some controversy regarding the use of Panzers with IR equipment on the Western Front, although at least two instances are recorded. One of these took place on April 21, 1945. At two o'clock in the morning, 10 Panthers of Panzer Division 'Clausewitz' attacked a US anti-tank gun battery positioned on the Weser/Elbe Canal. The Americans were alerted, one Panther was hit and the advance stalled. The two IR-equipped Panthers then moved up into a good position. They located and destroyed the entire US gun battery, resulting in the crews and the infantry fleeing in panic. These Panthers followed up the attack by destroying a number of trucks and other support vehicles. The Panzer Division considered this a great success, as it illustrated the enormous possibilities of infrared vision technology. According to the US 407th Infantry Regiment's after action report, Red 129 stalled and its crew were all killed after they got out and tried to crank-start it. Note that this IR-capable Panther actually has the IR equipment storage box mounted to the right rear hull and fittings on the side of the mantle.

but had not requested the diesel version. This diesel version was apparently Dr Maybach's own idea and was being developed on Maybach funds.

"None of the personnel was aware of any consideration being given for the trial installations of a gas turbine in the Panther."

The report concludes with some 'general observations' concerning the Panther which are worthy of note: "The general consensus of opinion among allied observers is that the Panther was probably the best designed German tank. The heavier armour and greater firepower of the Tiger made it a formidable defensive vehicle but for an all-around offensive and defensive vehicle, the Panther, even with its troubles, was the best the Germans had produced.

"This conclusion was held by the Germans, too, as was brought out in the interrogation of Stieler von Heydekampf, ▶

PANTHER AUSF. G

With the Soviets closing in on Berlin during late April 1945, Adolf Hitler ordered Generalleutnant Ernst Käther to be the commander of the Berlin Defence Area. This Panther, Yellow 324, was a part of 'Kampfgruppe Käther' named after the commander.

PANTHER

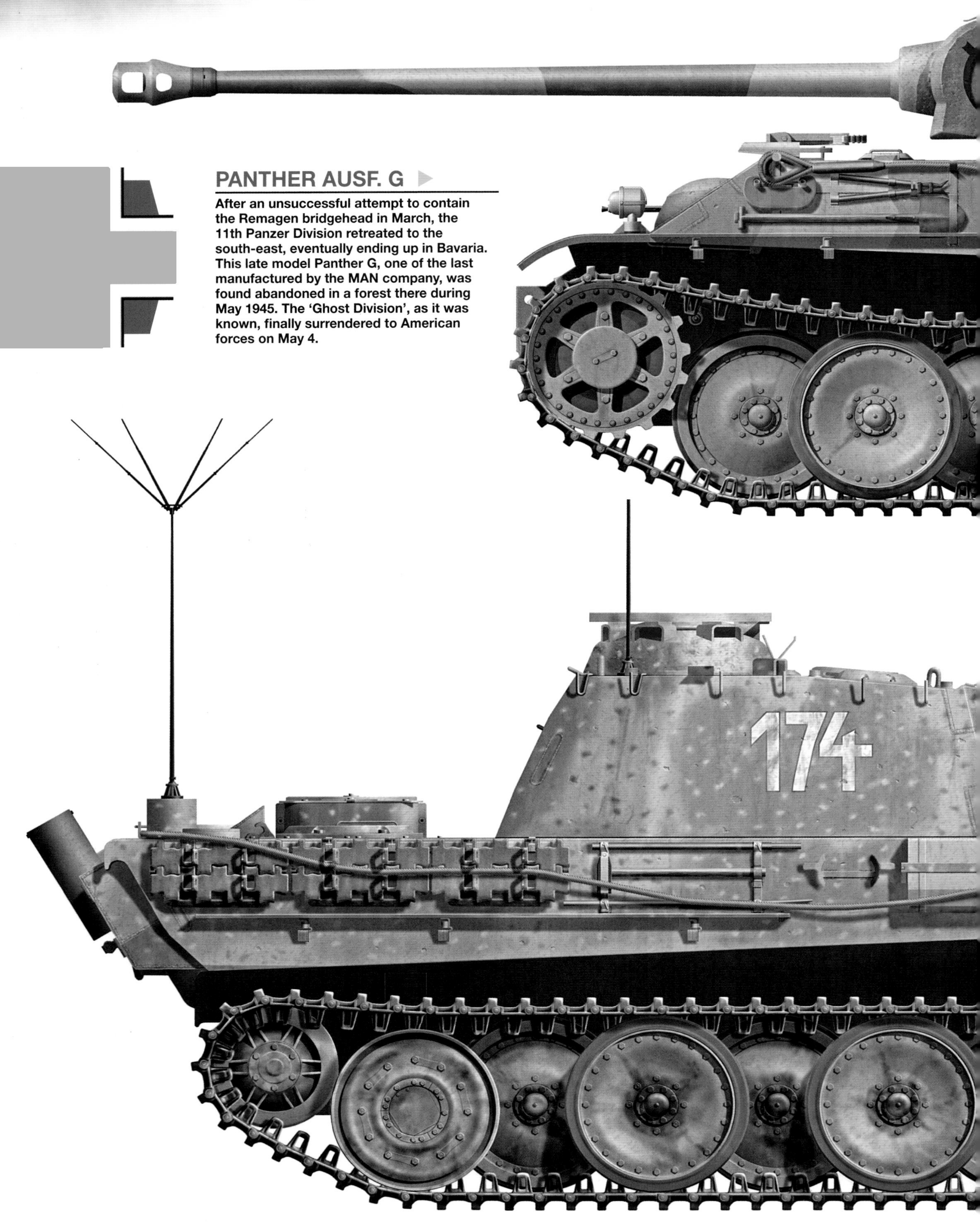

PANTHER AUSF. G

After an unsuccessful attempt to contain the Remagen bridgehead in March, the 11th Panzer Division retreated to the south-east, eventually ending up in Bavaria. This late model Panther G, one of the last manufactured by the MAN company, was found abandoned in a forest there during May 1945. The 'Ghost Division', as it was known, finally surrendered to American forces on May 4.

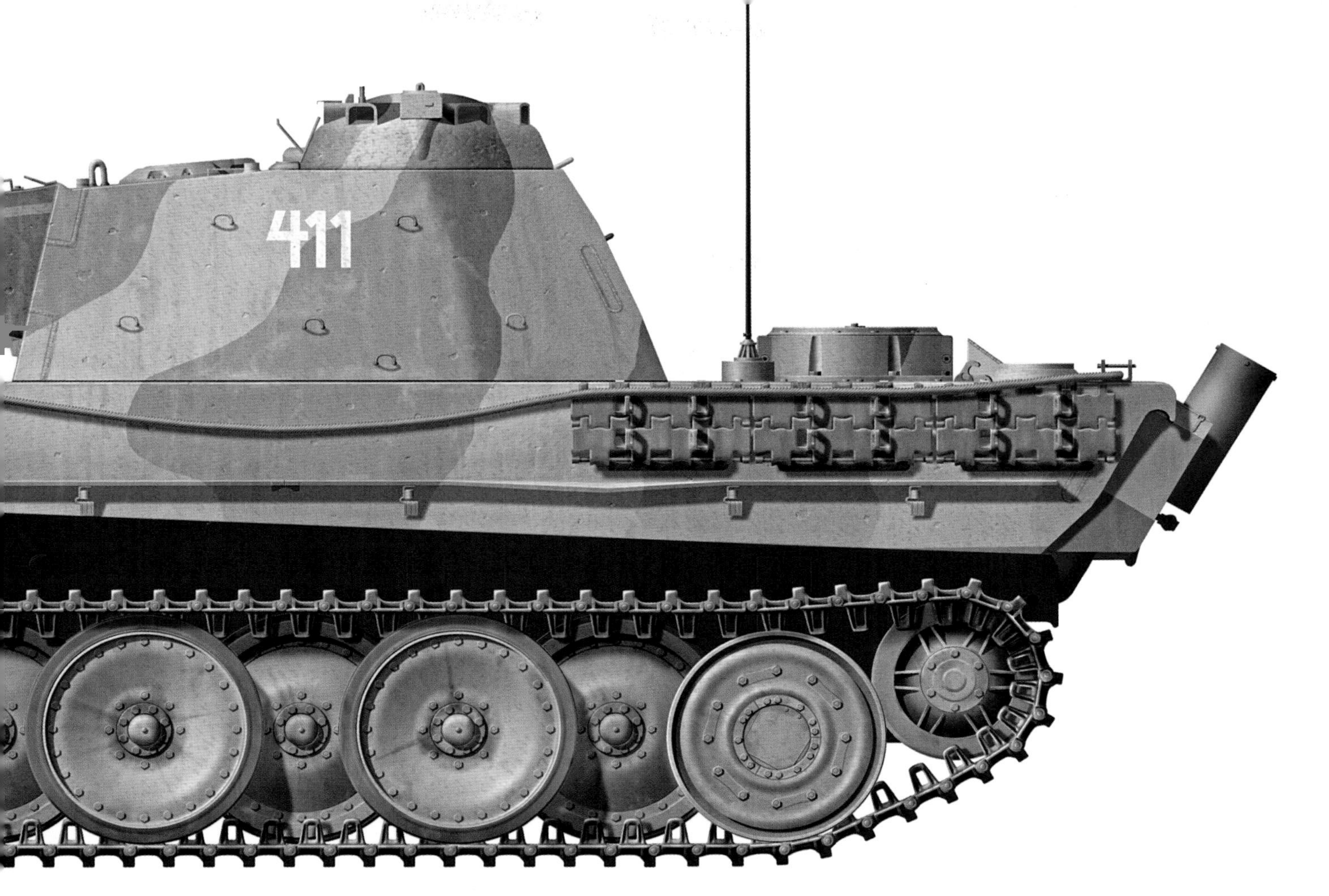

who gave production schedules for 1945 during which time the Panther was to be the high-production tank. Von Heydekampf, who was a production man, further stated that the general opinion of the OKH was that it was as cheap in man hours and money to build two 35- to 40-ton tanks as it was one 65- to 70-ton vehicle as represented by the Tiger.

"Herr Wiebeche volunteered the information that the Panther had been designed to cope with the Russian T-34. As this vehicle had caused the Germans a lot of trouble, the design of the T-34 hull and turret was copied as closely as possible in the design of the Panther. The fact that the Tiger II was modelled after the Panther, the entire engine compartment layout being followed as closely as possible, is further testimony to the high regard the OKH had for the Panther design. The E-100 designed by Adler also copied the Panther hull design." ●

PANTHER AUSF. G

Fighting during the last month of the war became close to impossible for the Germans. During April, Panzer Regiment 24 reported that fuel supplies were extremely low, and that its units were sometimes completely without fuel stocks. This made any movement or combat operations impossible and 12 Panthers had to be abandoned through lack of fuel. Another problem was the lack of infantry support which forced the regiment to use the tanks as a part of a defensive line. Although often successful, this resulted in losses and excessive wear on the tanks. Finally, after a fighting withdrawal from Vienna, they blew up the last few Panthers on the northern outskirts of the small town of Lietzen on May 9, 1945. Note that White 174, a late production Befehlspanther, had one steel wheel set as a part of its suspension and that it was configured for IR equipment.

STUG IV

Essentially a StuG III casemate on a Panzer IV chassis, the StuG IV proved to be a useful stopgap vehicle that was both easy to make and effective on the battlefield.

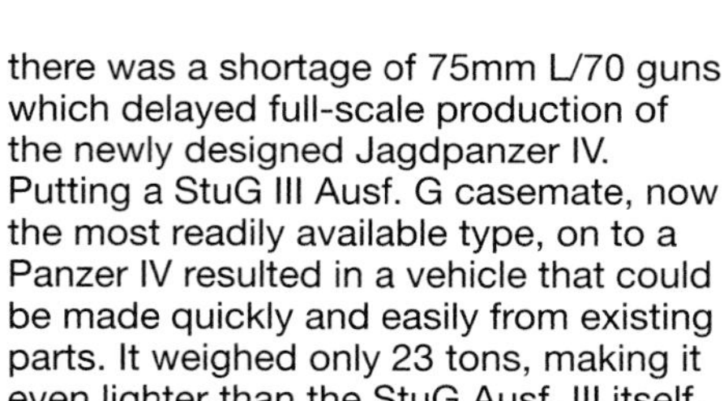

Technological advances came rapidly during the Second World War and some vehicles were inevitably left behind during the race for thicker armour and larger guns. One such vehicle was the StuG III Ausf. F – more Ausf. F superstructures had been manufactured than there were Panzer III chassis available to put them on.

Therefore Krupp drew up a plan in February 1943 to put these casemates on to Panzer IV chassis instead. However, the scheme was suspended in October 1943 when Hitler ordered that a new casemate be designed specifically for the Panzer IV, resulting in the Jagdpanzer IV.

The StuG IV idea was revived in late November 1943, however, when StuG III manufacturer Alkett suffered severe damage during a bombing raid and there was a shortage of 75mm L/70 guns which delayed full-scale production of the newly designed Jagdpanzer IV. Putting a StuG III Ausf. G casemate, now the most readily available type, on to a Panzer IV resulted in a vehicle that could be made quickly and easily from existing parts. It weighed only 23 tons, making it even lighter than the StuG Ausf. III itself.

The StuG IV had a crew of four: the commander in the left rear hull, the loader in the right rear hull, the gunner on the left side of the hull in the centre and the driver seated to the front left of the hull. It was armed with the 75mm StuK 40 L/48 gun with 63 rounds – the same main gun as

1943-1945

STUG IV

'Elsbeth' was among 307 tanks and self-propelled guns captured intact by the Red Army in Latvia following the collapse of the Courland pocket in May 1945. It had belonged to either the 12th or 14th Panzer Division and was lined up alongside numerous other vehicles for inspection by Red Army officers during May/June at Stende. All together, the Soviets captured 150,000 men, including 28 generals, 75 aircraft, 1427 field guns, 219 armoured personnel carriers, 4281 motor vehicles and a huge quantity of other equipment. Taking the pocket had cost the Soviets 320,000 soldiers – killed, wounded or missing in action – 2388 tanks, 659 aircraft and 900 field guns.

STUG IV

Red 4334 belonged to the 4th SS Polizei Panzergrenadier Division as part of Army Group South Ukraine during September 1944 when German forces in Turnu-Severin, Romania, were attempting to hold a defensive line against both Soviet and Romanian forces – the latter being their former allies. After the Soviets' assault on the Second Ukrainian Front with more than 900,000 men in late August, the Romanian Army had started to collapse. The country's King Michael led a coup d'état against the government, quickly made peace with the Russians, and declared war on Germany. Army Group South Ukraine was then attacked by both Soviet and Romanian forces and was forced to retreat towards the Carpathian Mountains. This afforded the Germans a good defensive line in the Transylvanian Alps but even this could not hold against large-scale Soviet assaults and the Germans were forced to fight a number of battles during their retreat towards Hungary.

the later Panzer IV and StuG III – plus a single 7.92mm MG 34 with 600 rounds for close defence. The engine was the usual Panzer IV powerplant, the V12 Maybach HL 120 TRM, and operational range was 210km with an internal fuel tank capable of holding 430 litres. Top speed was 40km/h. Armour protection on the casemate was the same as that of the StuG III, while the chassis armour was the same as that of the Panzer IV.

A total of 1108 StuG IVs were built by Krupp from December 1943 to May 1945, with another 31 being created from salvaged battle-damaged Panzer IV hulls. ●

JAGDPANZER IV

Intended as a replacement for the StuG III, the Jagdpanzer IV was a successful tank destroyer which ended up serving alongside its predecessor rather than supplanting it.

The success of the relatively inexpensive StuG III on the battlefield in the anti-tank role during 1942 meant it was desirable to create a new and improved tank destroyer based on the same concept. The ability to mount the Panther tank's 75mm KwK 42 L/70 was a key requirement, since the StuG III's casemate was too small to accept it.

Vogtländische Maschinenfabrik AG (Vomag), based in Plauen, eastern Germany, received a contract to design a tank destroyer based on the Panzer IV's running gear that could carry the 75mm gun in September 1942. A wooden model was shown to Hitler on May 13, 1943, which incorporated the vehicle's key features – a low height, sloped forward armour and a gun mantle designed to deflect incoming shells.

The design would include a 60mm thick upper plate sloped at 45 degrees and a 50mm lower plate angled at 55 degrees. The vehicle had a crew of four – commander, gunner, loader and driver – and in addition to its main gun with 79 shells it carried a single MG 42 with 1200 rounds. Traverse for the main gun was 12 degrees to either side. The engine was the usual V12 Maybach HL 120 TRM and with 470 litres of fuel brimming its tanks it could achieve a range of 210km by road or 130km cross-country. Overall weight was 24 tons and top speed was 40km/h, although average road speed was 25km/h and cross-country this dropped to just 15-18km/h.

Prototypes and pre-production models were built and trialled at the end of 1943 and, despite the previously mentioned delays which had resulted in the StuG IV, full production began in January 1944. Shortages of the Pak 42 L/70 meant early models had to be fitted with the shorter-barrelled 75mm Pak 39 L/43 or 75mm Pak 39 L/48 instead.

Between January 1944 and November 1944, Vomag built between 769 and 784 examples of the Jagdpanzer IV. The most produced version, between 930 and 940 built from August 1944 to April 1945, was fitted with the Pak 42 L/70. This was

JAGDPANZER IV/46

This Jagdpanzer IV was found by US forces abandoned in Chateaudun, Normandy, during the Operation Cobra breakout in August 1944. Red 212 had been left behind by the retreating Panzer Lehr Regiment and was missing its muzzle brake, which was probably removed by the Germans. The Panzer Lehr had been directly in the path of the breakout, which was preceded by a massive aerial bombardment involving some 2000 Allied bombers. The regiment's commander General Fritz Bayerlein reported that he had lost 950 men between July 24 and 25, with 50% killed or wounded by the carpet bombing raid and the remainder killed or wounded by a shattering artillery barrage involving around 1000 guns which followed and the attack of the US 1st Infantry Division itself. Following the breakout, the Panzer Lehr was withdrawn to Fontainebleau for rest and refit.

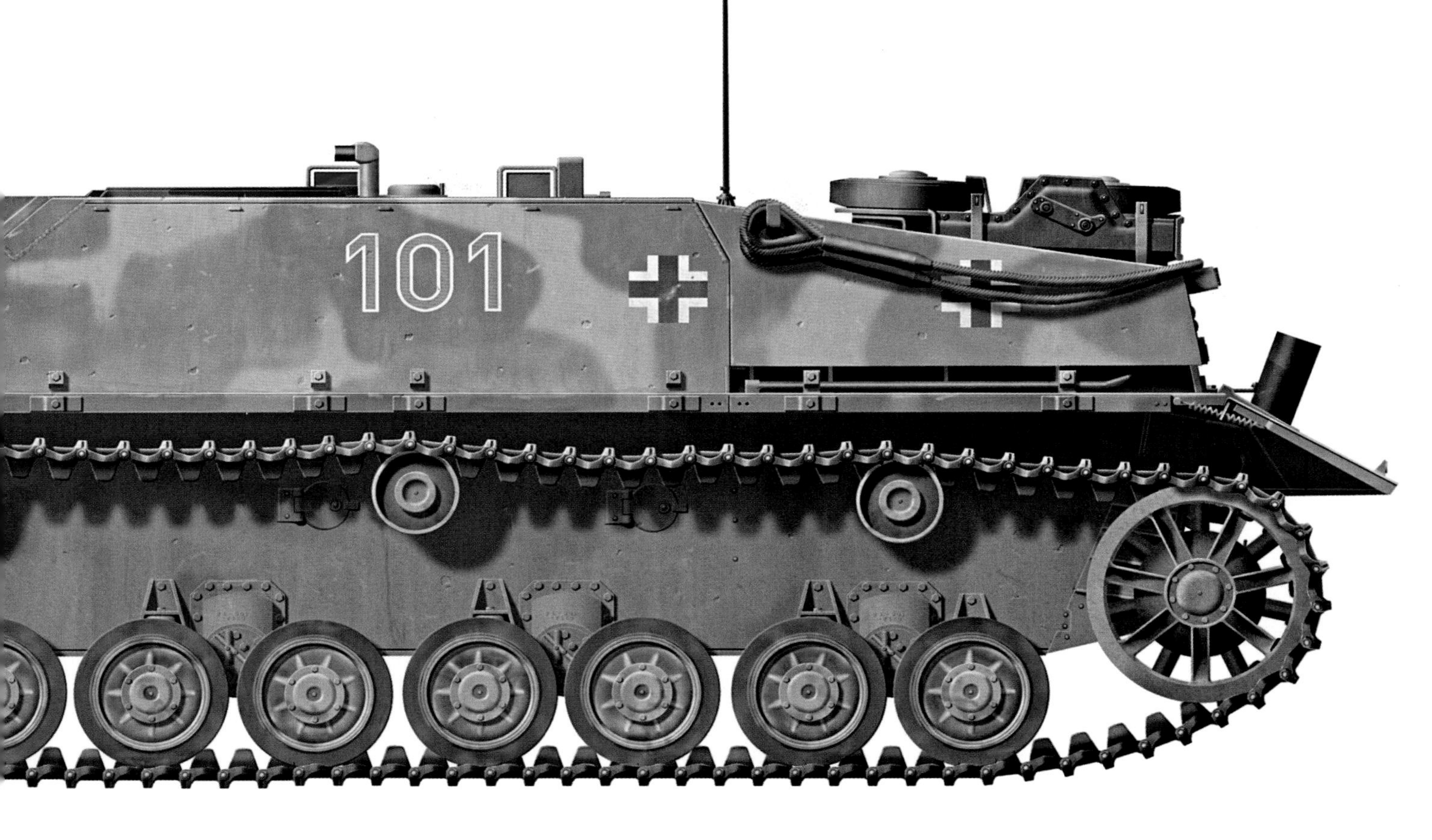

renamed the Panzer IV/70 (V), with the 'V' standing for Vomag. The larger, heavier gun meant there was only room for 60 shells and overall weight increased to 25.5 tons.

A third variant, known as the Panzer IV/70 (A) was created in July 1944 when Nibelungenwerk was switching from Panzer IV to Panzer IV/70 production. In order to speed things up, rather than just using the Panzer IV's running gear a complete Panzer IV chassis had Vomag's Jagdpanzer IV superstructure simply dropped on to it. This resulted in an awkward-looking vehicle that was about 40cm taller than Vomag had intended. Weight was greater too at 27 tons, but the extra space created by the height increase meant up to 90 shells could be carried. Maximum speed was reduced to 38km/h. Just 278 of these were built between August 1944 and March 1945. ●

PANZER IV/70 ▲

Red 101 was a Panzer IV/70 fitted out to Befehlswagen standard and surrendered to the Canadian army in May 1945. It belonged to schwere Panzerjäger-Abteilung 655, a unit formed in March 1943 with the Nashorn open-topped tank destroyer. It fought on the Eastern Front until the end of 1944 when it was withdrawn for a rest. Thereafter, it served on the Western Front and a unit roster dated April 23, 1945 shows that it had 10 Panzer IV/70s and five Jagdpanthers on charge at that time. Red 101 is unusual as it was one of the few vehicles in the units sporting a tactical number.

JAGDPANTHER

The most successful attempt to create a tank destroyer with an 88mm gun, the Jagdpanther was a fearsome vehicle but its introduction was delayed by administrative problems and when it did enter production it was too complex and costly to build in large numbers.

Early efforts to fit an 88mm anti-tank gun to a mobile chassis had resulted in a series of unsatisfactory vehicles – specifically the lightweight, open-topped and poorly armoured Nashorn based on components of both the Panzer III and Panzer IV, and the mechanically unreliable heavyweight Ferdinand/Elefant.

Therefore, even before series production of MAN's Panther design had begun, Krupp was awarded a contract to create a tank destroyer armed with an 88mm gun based on its chassis in August 1942. The timescale was tight – with the German Waffenamt requiring completion of the first vehicle by June 1943 and the commencement of full production the following month.

The project was handed over to Daimler-Benz towards the end of 1942 since that company was already engaged in production of the Panther. Daimler-Benz itself managed to produce the detailed design, reducing the casemate's originally specified 100mm frontal armour to a single 80mm slope and setting the thickness of the lower plate and superstructure sides at 50mm. The running gear and underpinnings of the production Panther remained unchanged.

On May 23, 1943, the project was shuffled on to yet another company –

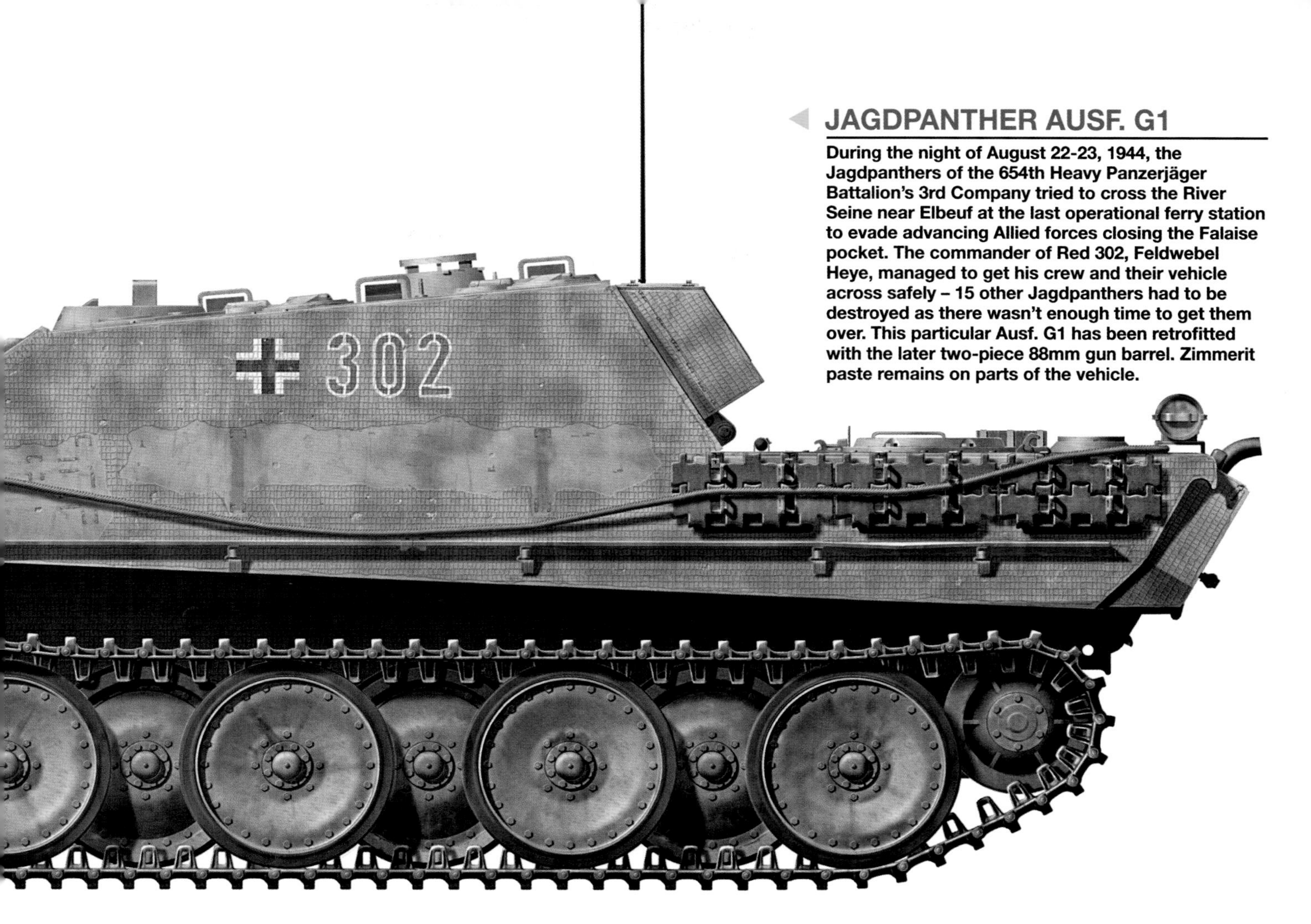

JAGDPANTHER AUSF. G1

During the night of August 22-23, 1944, the Jagdpanthers of the 654th Heavy Panzerjäger Battalion's 3rd Company tried to cross the River Seine near Elbeuf at the last operational ferry station to evade advancing Allied forces closing the Falaise pocket. The commander of Red 302, Feldwebel Heye, managed to get his crew and their vehicle across safely – 15 other Jagdpanthers had to be destroyed as there wasn't enough time to get them over. This particular Ausf. G1 has been retrofitted with the later two-piece 88mm gun barrel. Zimmerit paste remains on parts of the vehicle.

Braunschweig-based Mühlenbau und Industrie AG (MIAG) – for prototype construction. A full-scale mockup constructed by Daimler-Benz was shown to Hitler on October 20, 1943, before the first MIAG-built prototypes followed, the first later that month and the second in November. Series production then commenced in January 1944 using the Panther Ausf. G chassis.

However, bombing raids on MIAG's factories reduced output of the new Jagdpanther to a crawl and two further plants – Maschinenfabrik Niedersachsen-Hannover (MNH) and Maschinenbau und Bahnbedarf (MBA) in Potsdam-Drewitz – were also tasked with building the vehicle from November 1944 onwards.

The main gun, mounted in a central mantlet with a traverse of 12 degrees to either side, was the 88mm Pak 43/3 L/71 similar to the main gun of the Tiger II. For close-up defence, a single 7.92mm MG 34 machine gun was installed in a ball mount on the right-hand side of the frontal plate. The Jagdpanther carried 60 rounds for the former and 1200 rounds for the latter.

JAGDPANTHER AUSF. G1

Red 321, another vehicle of the 654's 3rd Company retrofitted with the two-piece 88mm, also escaped from Falaise and is pictured here as it appeared at Grafenwöhr in Germany during October 1944. It was commanded by Leutnant Prigge and was eventually knocked out at Friesen by an anti-tank gun on October 22.

JAGDPANTHER

JAGDPANZER V JAGDPANTHER AUSF. G1

Allied forces found this Jagdpanther, belonging to the 9th SS Panzer Division 'Hohenstaufen' immobilised on the streets of Terschen – today known as Děčín in the Czech Republic. Its gunner (some sources say loader) was future Nobel Prize for Literature winner Günther Grass. Grass was drafted into the Waffen-SS as a 17-year-old in late 1944. After the war he became a social democrat and pacifist, winning the Nobel Prize in 1999 for having written novels such as The Tin Drum, Cat and Mouse and Dog Years – the Danzig Trilogy – all of which deal with the Second World War and the Nazi regime in one way or another. The 'Hohenstaufen' fought in the last major German offensive of the war – the attempted liberation of Budapest. It then withdrew to Austria before surrendering to the US army at Steyer.

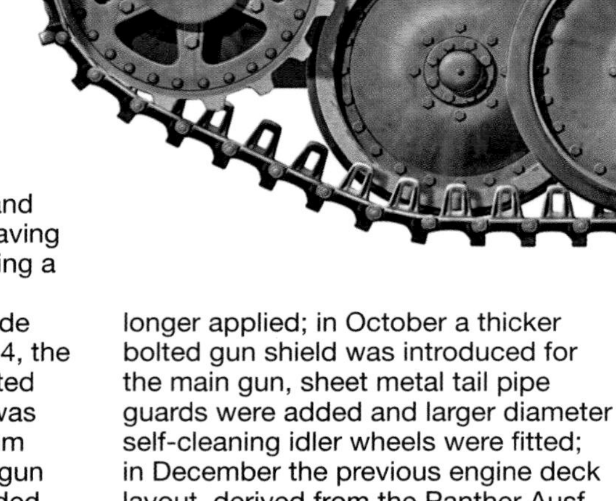

As with the Panther, the engine fitted was the V12 Maybach HL 230 P30 developing 690hp. This offered a good power-to-weight ratio, since the vehicle weighed 45.5 tons – just slightly heavier than the Panther's own 44.8 tons. Theoretical top speed was 46km/h but this could not be sustained for any length of time without damaging the vehicle's drive train. In practice, road speed was around 25km/h with cross-country speed being more like 15km/h. A fuel capacity of 700 litres resulted in a range of 160km on the road and 80km cross-country.

The vehicle had a crew of five – commander, gunner, loader, driver and radio operator – the driver initially having two vision slots and the gunner having a periscope on the vehicle's roof.

A range of modifications was made during production – in February 1944, the driver's second vision slot was deleted and a central rear towing coupling was added; in May the single-piece 88mm gun was replaced with a two-piece gun and a pair of cooling pipes were added to the engine manifold; in June, three Pilze were welded to the roof of the superstructure for mounting a jib boom crane; from September Zimmerit was no longer applied; in October a thicker bolted gun shield was introduced for the main gun, sheet metal tail pipe guards were added and larger diameter self-cleaning idler wheels were fitted; in December the previous engine deck layout, derived from the Panther Ausf. A, was upgraded to that of the Panther Ausf. G and flame-suppressing mufflers were added. Finally, in February 1945 a stowage box was deleted from the left

JAGDPANTHER AUSF. G2

Led by Hauptmann von Schlippenbach, the II./Panzer Lehr Regiment 130 was fortunate enough to receive 35 brand new Jagdpanthers straight off the MIAG production line at Braunschweig in early April 1945. These included Yellow 721. The 5th, 6th, 7th and 8th Companies got eight each, while the Staff Company received three. The unit left Braunschweig on April 8 and drove west on the autobahn for about 35km before stopping to form a west-facing defensive line in the area of Edemissen-Hämelerwald-Burgdorf. Three days later, on the 11th, the line was attacked by elements of the US 11th Cavalry Regiment and the 5th Armored Division. By the end of the day only nine of the original 35 Jagdpanthers remained operational.

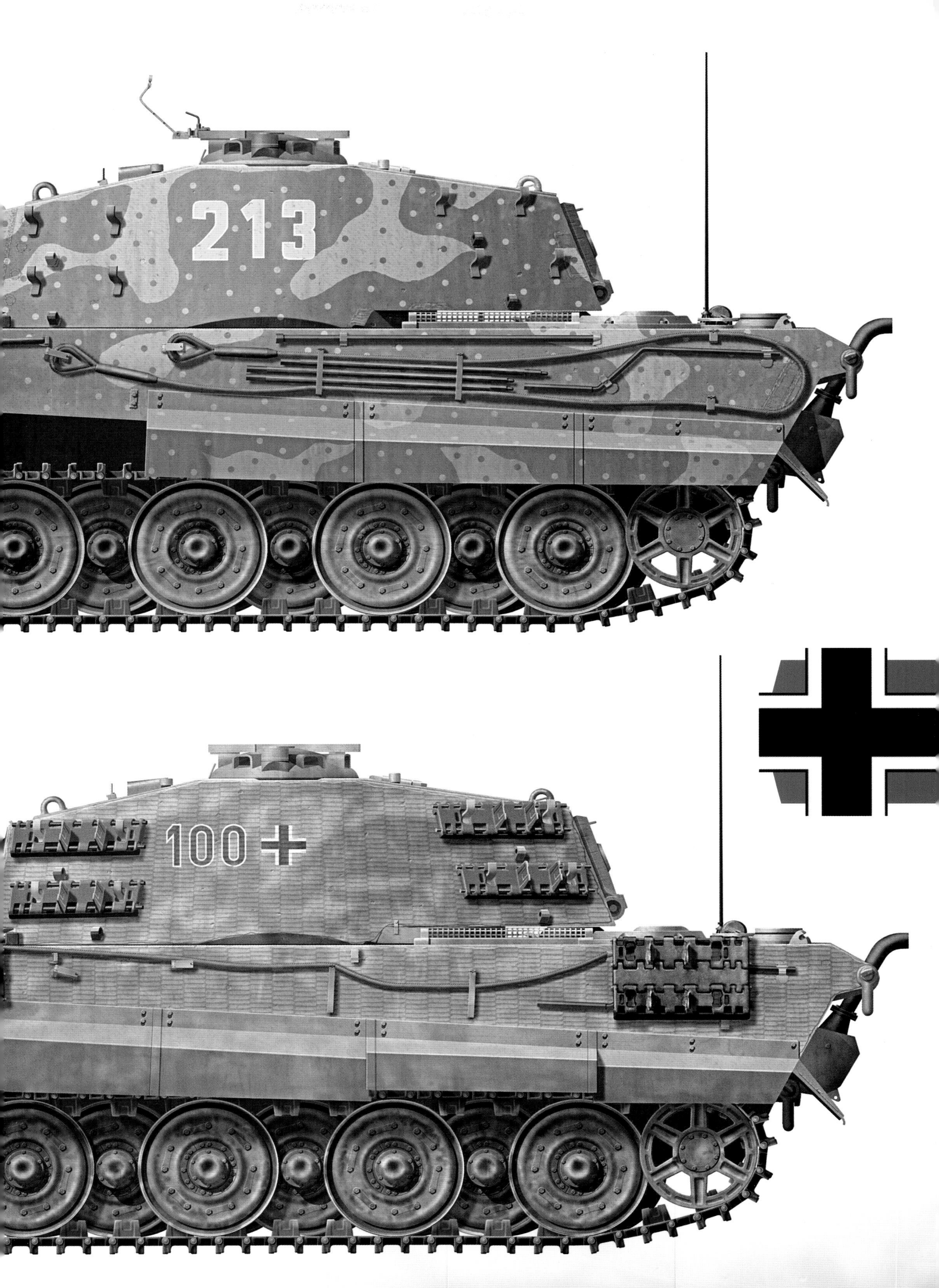
213
100

TIGER II AUSF. B

Commanded by SS-Hauptsturmführer Rolf von Westerhagen of the 501st SS Heavy Panzer Battalion's 3rd Company, Blue 331 was knocked out during the unsuccessful German offensive to liberate Budapest – Operation Frühlingserwachen or 'Spring Awakening'. Afterwards, the Russians located all the knocked-out and abandoned German armoured vehicles, and marked this particular Tiger II as No. 93 for their records. This is how it appeared in March 1945 in the Lake Balaton area of Hungary.

dark yellow, with areas of red brown, RAL 8017, and olive green, RAL 6003, painted over it. Previously, Tiger IIs had been delivered in an all-over covering of dark yellow and it had been up to each individual unit to add their camouflage pattern of choice. In addition, where the interior of earlier Tiger IIs had received an all-over coat of ivory white paint, tanks produced after August 1944 were left in their base coat of red primer inside.

As with all other German tanks, in September 1944 the application of Zimmerit ceased. From October 9, 1944, all Tiger IIs received a thinner coat of paint than they had before and from October 31, Henschel was required to stop using RAL 7028 and the other two colours were simply applied directly over the red primer instead.

In December, the companies responsible for making the Tiger II's armour were told to apply a dark green undercoat – RAL 6003 – before sending the components to Henschel for assembly. At Henschel, a camouflage pattern of RAL 8017 and RAL 7028 would then be applied over it. A minor modification also approved at this point was the addition of armour plates to be fitted over the rear deck air intake gratings. The goal was to prevent splinters from shells and other stray fragments of metal from entering the intakes. However, it seems that this modification was not generally adopted.

From January 1945, Tiger II turrets had a new metal guard installed above the aperture for the gunsight. This extended

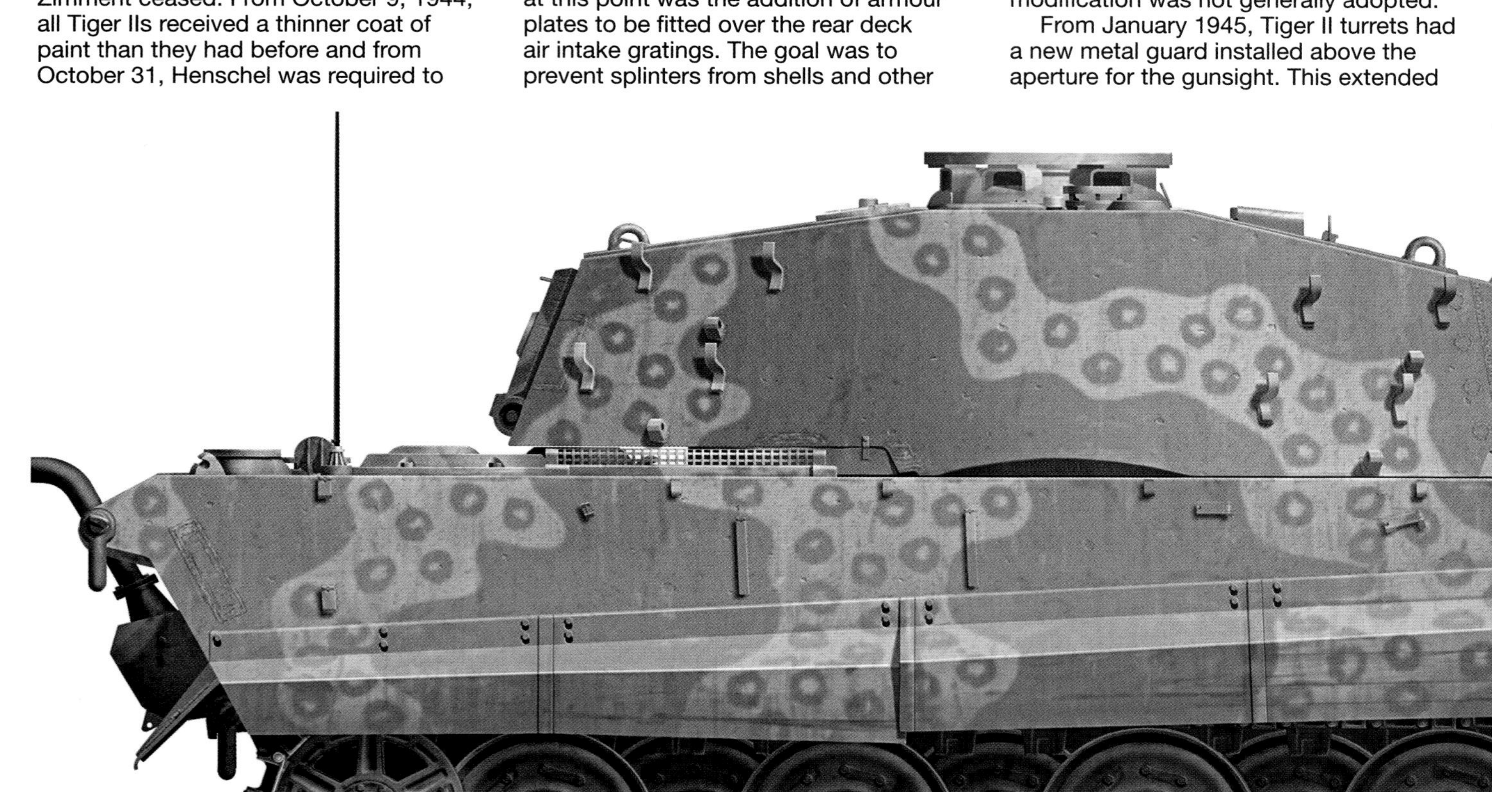

quite a way from the turret face and was intended primarily to prevent rainwater from obscuring the sight but with the added benefit that it also shielded the gunner from the rays of the rising or setting sun to a greater degree. Finally, just before production ceased in March 1945, another new track design was devised and approved for the Tiger II.

Overall, production of the Tiger II at Henschel had continued steadily until September 22 when the first of five bombing raids resulted in severe disruption to the assembly line. Further raids on September 27 and 28, and October 2 and 7 annihilated 95% of the Henschel factory. Efforts to repair and rebuild began immediately but another raid on December 15 resulted in further delays. Henschel's subsidiary works and many of its suppliers also suffered damage in bombing raids, causing Tiger II production to be significantly curtailed.

By March 1945, when Henschel's production lines ceased to function, only the three prototypes and 489 series models – 492 tanks in total – had been built. ●

TIGER II AUSF. B

Tiger II of 3./schwere Panzer-Abteilung 510, Kassel area/Germany, April 17, 1945. This unnumbered but spectacularly camouflaged Tiger II was one of six brand new Tiger IIs that were collected at the Henschel factory in Wilhelmstal by the 510th Heavy Panzer Battalion's 3rd Company on March 29, 1945. It was probably spray-painted in this pattern by the crew after they left the factory. The 3rd Company was then involved in several skirmishes between March 30 and April 8. They disbanded on April 17 and this vehicle, together with another Tiger II, was abandoned by its crew and blown up.

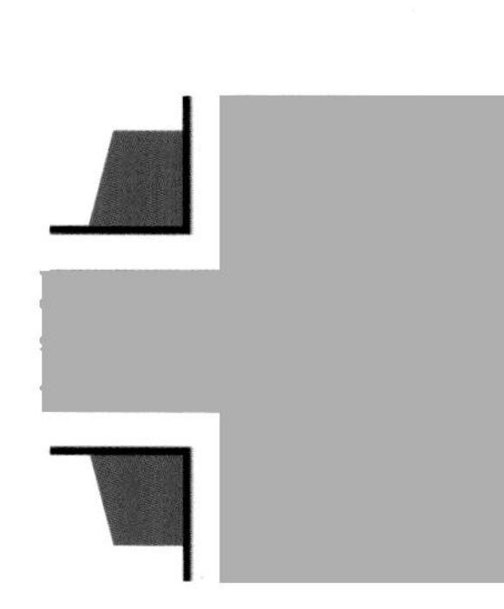

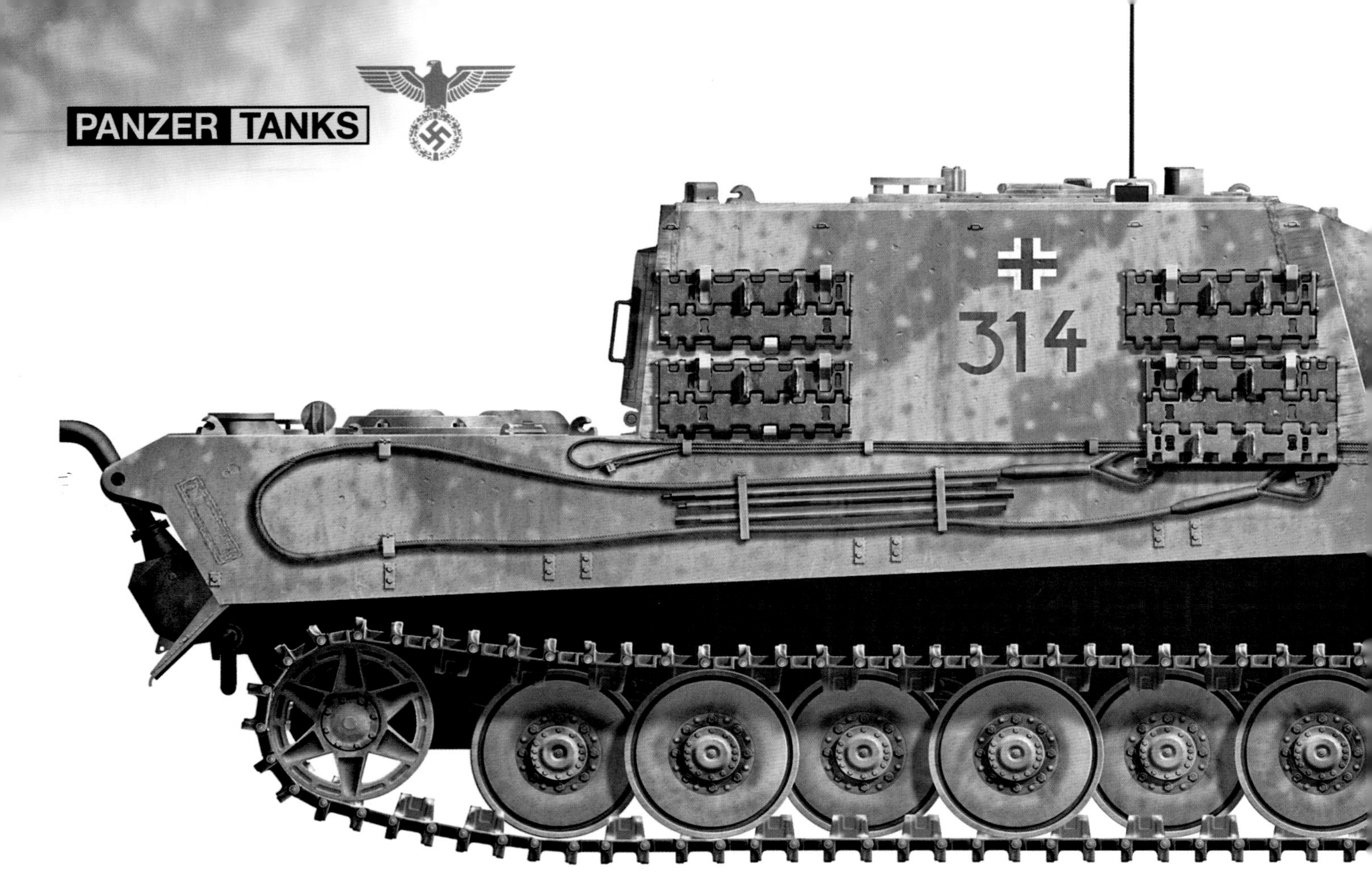

JAGDTIGER

Produced in only small numbers right at the end, the Jagdtiger was nevertheless the heaviest armoured fighting vehicle to see combat during the Second World War.

1944-1945

The idea of building a super heavy tank destroyer armed with a 128mm gun had been talked about by the German army general staff since early 1942 but no progress was made towards constructing such a vehicle until it was discussed during a conference with Adolf Hitler on February 21, 1943. Hitler was enthusiastic about the proposal and approved the construction of prototypes. Since the design of the Tiger II was already well advanced by this point, it was decided that Henschel should use its chassis as the basis for the new vehicle.

It was eventually discovered, however, that the 128mm KwK L/55 – originally intended for the aborted superheavy tank 'Maus' – was simply too long for even the Tiger II's hull. As a result, this had to be stretched by 400mm to accommodate the weapon.

Although Henschel designed its own suspension unit for the Jagdtiger, Dr Ferdinand Porsche offered Hitler an alternative

JAGDTIGER

Black 314 of the 653rd Heavy Panzerjäger Battalion's 3rd Company, commanded by Feldwebel Erich Bonike, was with a group of five other Jagdtigers that was ordered to attack American positions in Morsbronn on the German-French border on March 16, 1945. Approaching the village, the unit was hit by heavy artillery fire, combined with an aerial attack from P-47 Thunderbolt fighter-bombers. Black 314, hull number 305012, was the last example built with the Porsche suspension system. Rather than being knocked out by the enemy, it suffered drive train problems. Unable to proceed with the attack, its crew drove it into a ditch and blew it up to prevent it from falling into enemy hands.

arrangement which he argued would be quicker to build, easier to maintain in the field and, above all, substantially cheaper.

While the Henschel arrangement required nine wheels per side with torsion bars running laterally from one side of the vehicle to the other, the Porsche design consisted of four bogies on each side, each with two wheels attached to them with a very short 1.075m torsion bar fitted to each unit running longitudinally – parallel with the wheels themselves.

Porsche claimed that the Henschel design required machining to very close tolerances so that both sides of the vehicle's hull matched up exactly, whereas this was not necessary for his design, since each bogie operated independently of all the others. The difference in cost, according to Porsche, was 866,000 RM per Henschel unit versus 462,000 RM per Porsche unit; and it took 360 man hours to build one Henschel unit versus 140 hours for the Porsche. There was even a weight saving of one ton overall using the Porsche unit rather than Henschel's.

Work on two prototypes was commenced in December 1943 – one with Henschel's suspension and the other with Porsche's. While the Porsche arrangement looked promising on paper, in practice the individual bogies were too weak to support the massive 74-ton weight of the vehicle. Nevertheless, 10 more examples with Porsche's

JAGDTIGER

Another Jagdtiger from 653rd Heavy Panzerjäger Battalion's 3rd Company, Black 323, was among three Jagdtigers which took up defensive positions in Neustadt, Germany, on March 22, 1945. As American armoured forces drove forwards, between them the trio managed to knock out a total of 25 tanks and tank destroyers for no losses. When the battle was over, cautiously advancing American soldiers of the 10th Armored Division found two of the Jagdtigers abandoned. 331 had been left in the middle of Landauer Strasse, while Black 323 was parked in a courtyard opposite. The latter had taken at least nine direct hits from armour-piercing rounds and three more from high-explosive shells but none of them had penetrated. The vehicle had been abandoned when it ran out of ammunition because its final drive had suffered damage, making it impossible to recover under the circumstances. The crew had sabotaged its gun before retreating. The 653rd finally surrendered its last four operational Jagdtigers to US forces between May 5 and May 7, 1945.

JAGDTIGER

Deployed as part of Panzer Group Hudel, White X7, of the 512th Heavy Panzer Battalion's 1st Company, joined German forces attempting to stop the US Army enlarging its Remagen bridgehead across the Rhine in late March 1945. Positioned along the Sieg River, the 512th attacked the 3rd Armored Division and then retreated, the Jagdtigers being used to fight a rearguard action – knocking out advancing Shermans at ranges of up to four kilometres. The 512th lost four Jagdtigers, three of them simply because they broke down, including White X7. The vehicle was abandoned in Obernephen on April 1. The remainder of the battalion would fight on for two more weeks before surrendering.

suspension were constructed before production switched permanently to the original Henschel design.

The Jagdtiger's gun had a 10-degree traverse to either side and 40 rounds of ammunition for it could be carried at any one time. Two loaders were needed to handle the shells, each of which consisted of a separate projectile and cased propellant charge.

Maximum armour thickness on the superstructure forward plate was 250mm, with 150mm on the glacis plate, 100mm on the lower front plate, 80mm on the side and rear, 50mm on the flat surface at the front and 40mm on the roof to centre and rear.

The vehicle was powered by the V12 Maybach HL 230 P30, developing 690hp, resulting in a claimed top speed of 42km/h on the road. With a full load of 860 litres of fuel in its internal tanks, range was 250km travelling by road or 145km travelling cross-country. Unfortunately the Jagdtiger struggled to achieve these speeds and distances without breaking down. Its huge weight put an intolerable strain on the components of its drive train – particularly the suspension and wheels. In addition, examples fitted with the Porsche suspension proved unsuitable for travel over rough terrain due to excessive vibration. Not only did this make life extremely uncomfortable for the crew, it also threw the gun out of calibration.

There were six crew – commander, gunner, loader, second loader, driver and radio operator – although in practice it sometimes operated with only five.

A total of between 70 and 88 Jagdtigers were built at the Nibelungenwerk factory, St Valentin, Austria, up to May 1945. These included four examples built with an 88mm Pak 43 L/71 gun due to shortages of the 128mm weapon. Modifications on the production line in July 1944 included the addition of four pairs of track hanger brackets welded on to the superstructure sides and the sheet metal guards around the exhausts being removed; in August a travel lock for the gun was added; from September, Zimmerit was no longer applied and a new track was fitted with corresponding new nine-tooth drive sprocket; from December the number of track hangers was increased to six pairs on both sides and finally in February 1945, Pilze sockets for mounting a two-ton jib boom were welded on to the top edge of the sides of the superstructure.

Even today, the Jagdtiger remains the heaviest armoured fighting vehicle ever to have entered series production. ●

JAGDTIGER

This Jagdtiger, White Y5 of the 512th Heavy Panzer Battalion's 3rd Company, fought in the defence of Paderborn as part of Panzer Group Hudel on April 1, 1945. The 3rd's five Jagdtigers managed to fight off attacks by the US 3rd Armored Division but the following day White Y5 was destroyed by American forces while another broke down. The last three vehicles were loaded on to railway carriages and transported to the Harz mountains, where they broke down one by one between April 10 and 15. Many of the 512th's crews complained bitterly about the Jagdtiger's issues – including Tiger I ace Otto Carius, who wrote about his experiences in his book Tigers in the Mud. Carius had been used to a rotating turret and quickly became frustrated with having to turn the entire vehicle for aiming while under constant pressure from the enemy. On the other hand, assault gun ace Albert Ernst later said that the Jagdtiger made him feel invincible with its exceptionally powerful gun and massive armour protection.

COLOUR CHART

RAL 7008
Graugrün

RAL 7021
Panzegrau

RAL 7028
Dunkelgelb

RAL 8002
Olivegrün

RAL 8017
Rotbraun

RAL 8020
Braungelb